WOOLDRIDGE(S.W.) and
HUTCHINGS (G.E.)
London's countryside

London's Countryside

1 The North Downs near Reigate. Note the characteristic vegetation on the scarp face and the limit of cultivation (normally the line of the Pilgrims' Way)

London's Countryside

GEOGRAPHICAL FIELD WORK FOR STUDENTS
AND TEACHERS OF GEOGRAPHY

S. W. WOOLDRIDGE
C.B.E., D.SC., F.G.S.

*Fellow of King's College, London, and Professor of Geography,
University of London King's College. Chairman of the Executive
Committee of the Field Studies Council*

and

GEOFFREY E. HUTCHINGS
F.G.S., F.R.G.S.

*Warden of the Juniper Hall Field Centre
of the Field Studies Council*

METHUEN AND CO LTD
11 NEW FETTER LANE E.C.4

First published February 21, 1957
Reprinted 1964

I.2

CATALOGUE NO. 02/5886/34

Printed and bound in Great Britain by
Butler & Tanner Ltd, Frome and London

DEDICATED TO

F. H. C. BUTLER
FOUNDER OF THE
FIELD STUDIES COUNCIL
AND
A. G. T. OAKLEY
ITS PRESENT SECRETARY

Contents

Illustrations

Preface

•••

Our object in writing this book is simple and definite. Both of us have spent much of our time during recent years in field teaching either with university field classes or with school and other parties under the aegis of the Field Studies Council. Wholly convinced as we are of the Council's objectives and methods we are yet inevitably conscious that unless we can hand the method on to an increasing number of colleagues the progress of field studies is halted at the very outset. We are both embarrassed and in the result over-worked by repeated requests to conduct parties over our 'teaching ground'. But we are anxious to secure that other teachers shall carry on the method, and in this book we have sought to assist them in this work. The greatest single obstacle, in our judgement, to field work in schools is the reluctance of the teacher to fare forth into unknown country with its double problem of finding the way and knowing what to see and what to say. We have therefore given explicit directions for a dozen walking routes and have essayed the more difficult task of a written running commentary. When in the field with a party one is guided and inspired by the need and mood of the moment, but our colleagues complain that we are, in fact, prepared for the work by prior study, whereas they must often 'start from scratch'. The gap thus implied we have sought in some measure to fill.

Further, we have not been without hope of enlisting the interest of a wider field of country lovers and walkers. There has grown up in recent years a large topographical literature in Britain. Much of this 'nonstopography', as it has been called in *Punch*, is of very limited assistance in forming any real comprehension of the country. In the attempt to be 'humane' it contents itself all too often with detached gobbets of local history and folk-lore; rarely is much attention given to the fundamental geological build of the country or to the superstructure which modern geographers have developed on this foundation. We venture at least to hope that the approach we have adopted may prove of value and interest to the naturalist and the local historian. The aim is regional synthesis and though this depends largely upon labours in the library and map-room, it cannot dispense with sensitive field observation.

All those, whether our own countrymen or visitors from overseas, who value the heritage of the English countryside will find profit in approaching it as something to be studied rather than merely visited and savoured. Other regions of Britain no doubt present landscapes of bolder and more dramatic lines, yet from many points of view south-east England is the most important region of Britain, and in any case it presents an unparalleled educational opportunity in view of the fact of Greater London and its population. Approximately one in four of the schoolchildren of the country live in or within reach of the country we have sought to describe and explain.

The authors desire to express their cordial thanks to Miss A. J. Dunn, formerly Secretary at Juniper Hall, and Miss V. J. Hodgson, Field Assistant, for welcome assistance in the preparation of this book.

JUNIPER HALL

Introduction

It may be helpful if we here comment briefly on the general plan of the book and give an indication of how we think it might be used by teachers. The first two chapters deal in outline with the physiography and historical geography of the Weald and London Basin respectively. Brief guidance is also offered on the interpretation of the vegetation communities.

Of the following twelve routes Nos. 1–4 deal with the country most readily studied from the Juniper Hall Field Centre. We naturally hope that an increasing number of parties will find it possible to use the residential and laboratory facilities of the Centre and thus make a brief consolidated study of the classic ground of the 'Surrey Hills', but the four routes have been arranged to be conducted, if desired, as single day excursions.

To develop 'an eye for country', in the geographer's sense, it is essential to use the comparative method. Working therefore from this small area as a basis we have extended the study westward to the Guildford area (Route 5) and eastward to the Darent and Medway Gaps (Routes 6, 7 and 8). To complete the study of the Northern Weald we have also included a route (No. 9) to form an introduction to the country of the High or Central Weald.

Finally, we have included three North London routes (Nos. 10, 11 and 12) in country very different in its geological basis and physiographic expression from the Weald, though preserving a fairly close parallel as an environment of human settlement.

It will be obvious that many more areas offer themselves for inclusion, but we have been concerned not to make the book too unhandily large for field use and we shall welcome the opportunity, if our first venture proves serviceable, of publishing the details of further routes. Nevertheless, those we have chosen present a tolerably complete and balanced introduction to south-east England in its wider sense. The chief omission which we shall seek opportunity to repair is the glacial drift country north and east of London. This, however, is difficult ground, not really suited to those beginning to learn the craft of field observation. Route 10 touches lightly on the complexities of 'drift geology'.

If we have successfully indicated the method, the best, and indeed the only, reward we would ask is that others will explore areas we have left untouched and work out routes for themselves. In any case we have not attempted to do the teacher's work for him, leaving him to adapt our method to the needs of his classes. It will probably be thought that much of our material is too difficult for elementary classes, but it is only the teacher who knows the background of his own class who can act as 'transformer' whether in a downward or an upward direction. For our own part we do not regard the material we have presented as suitable only for sixth-form or university use. At present it is only at these two levels that any adequate quantity or quality of field work is attempted. It is not less necessary in the Secondary Modern School, nor is it clear why the children of our Primary Schools should be wholly deprived of their heritage in our countryside and its geographical, historical and biological significance.

2 Juniper Hall Field Centre near Dorking, Surrey

I Physiography of the London Countryside

Before describing in detail the country to be traversed on each of the excursion routes it will be useful to give a general picture of those parts of the Weald and the London Basin to which this series of excursions is confined. The basis of such a general study is necessarily geological, and the reader should first become acquainted with names of the stratigraphical divisions of the rocks in the region, their order of sequence and the variations in their lithological character. This is summarized in the table on pp. 4 and 5. The distribution of the different kinds of rock over the surface of the ground is shown in the geological maps (Figs. 1 and 2), while their relative thickness and vertical disposition is represented in numerous cross-sections or 'transects' such as those shown in Figs. 3, 20, 26 and 30.

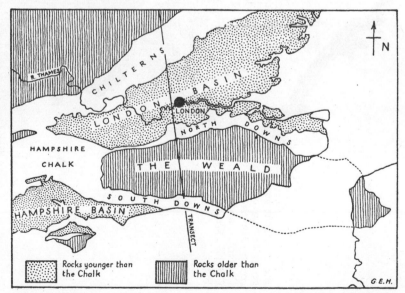

Fig. 1. The broad elements in the structure of South-east England

1

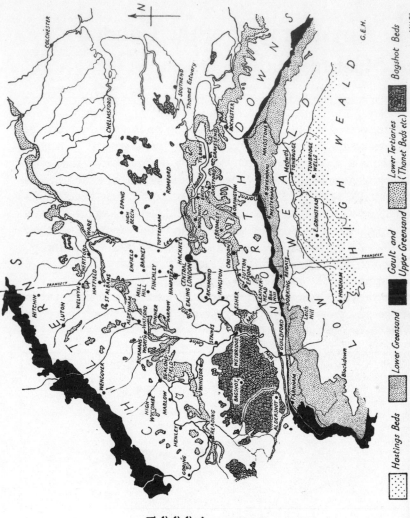

Fig. 2. Generalized geological map of the country between the Chilterns and the Central Weald (cf. Fig. 3)

Hastings Beds

Lower Greensand

Gault and Upper Greensand

Lower Tertiaries (Thanet Beds etc.)

Bagshot Beds

Weald Clay, Chalk and London Clay are left white.

MILES

0   10   20   30   40

G.E.M.

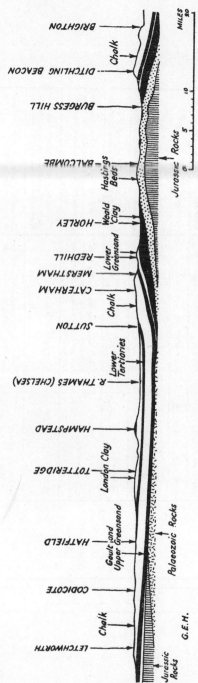

Fig. 3. Section across the London Basin and the Weald

2

TABLE OF GEOLOGICAL FORMATIONS EXPOSED IN THE WEALD AND THE LONDON BASIN

CHRONOLOGICAL DIVISIONS	NAMES OF SUBDIVISIONS	DESCRIPTION	LOCALITIES
PLIOCENE	PEBBLE GRAVEL	Gravel, largely of Eocene pebbles (Flint), locally with Lower Greensand quartz pebbles & chert.	Caps highest summits of Tertiary country, generally at about 400 ft. O.D. elevation.
	LENHAM BEDS	Sand or shingle containing Flint cobbles and fragments, pebbles derived from Eocene deposits, & Fragments of Greensand material	Plateaux of North Downs & the Chilterns on Flats at c. 600 ft. O.D. Notably Headley & Netley Heaths, Surrey.
	BARTON SAND	Sand.	Between Aldershot & Chobham.
	BRACKLESHAM BEDS	Laminated clay & sand.	Pirbright (NW of Guildford).
	BAGSHOT BEDS	Fine quartzose sand with local pebble beds.	Country N & NW of Guildford, Oxshott Heath, Surrey, Hampstead, Epping Forest & other high ground in the London Basin.
EOCENE	CLAYGATE BEDS	Alternate layers of sand & clay.	Outliers on higher ground of London Clay & outcrops below Bagshots.
	LONDON CLAY	Clay; blue-grey, weathering to dull brown on exposure. Contains calcareous concretions ('septaria') & much iron pyrites.	Widely exposed throughout London Basin, though concealed over large areas by Pleistocene & Recent deposits.
	BLACKHEATH BEDS	Flint pebbles & sand.	Plateau of NW Kent; outcrops at margin of London Clay; outliers on North Downs. No northern outcrop.
	READING BEDS (= WOOLWICH BEDS of Kent & SE London)	Pale-coloured sands & mottled clay. Occasional pebble beds. Shell beds in SE London & Kent areas.	Outcrops along both N & S margins of London Clay mass,
	THANET BEDS	Fine-grained sands.	Southern edge of Tertiaries. Wide outcrops & outliers on Chalk in Kent.
	UPPER CHALK	Pure white chalk with abundant Flint (silica), the latter commonly in horizontal bands at regular intervals. The Chalk Rock is a layer of hard chalk at the base of the U.C.	Dip-slopes of North Downs and Chilterns. Chalk Rock best seen in its outcrop along Chilterns escarpment,

TERTIARY

				...tent. No Flint in L.C.	
SECONDARY (MESOZOIC)	LOWER CRETACEOUS	UPPER GREENSAND		Sandy limestone or malmstone of variable composition. Green colour (where present) due to unaltered glauconite.	Base of Chalk escarpments, in places forming a distinct platform.
		GAULT		Stiff blue-grey clay at base; pale marly clay above. Phosphatic & pyritic nodules.	Floor of Chalk scarp vale.
		LOWER GREEN-SAND	FOLKESTONE BEDS	Fine & coarse sands, red, gold to white. Frequently current-bedded. Irregular bands of dark brown ironstone ('Carstone').	Outcrop mainly low ground adjacent to Gault. Elevated tracts at Ightham, Limpsfield, Westcott & St. Martha's.
			SANDGATE BEDS AND BARGATE BEDS	Loamy sand & fullers earth in E. Surrey. In W. Surrey the equivalent Bargate Beds consist of sand & coarse calcareous sandstone.	Narrow outcrop & scattered outliers in W. Kent; well developed nr. Redhill. Bargate type begins W. of Dorking with outcrop greatly expanded around Godalming.
			HYTHE BEDS	Sand, sandstone & chert. In Mid-Kent, calcareous 'ragstone'.	Irregular outcrop, forming generally the scarped upland parallel to the North Downs.
			ATHERFIELD CLAY	Clay & silty clay, difficult to distinguish from Weald Clay beneath.	Base of Hythe Beds scarp, where not obscured by slipped sandstone.
		WEALDEN	WEALD CLAY	Clay & shale with local beds of sand, sandstone or limestone. Nodules & bands of ironstone also occur.	Surface of this thick formation is the extensive plain of the Weald between hill ranges of the Lower Greensand & the Hastings Beds.
			HASTINGS BEDS — TUNBRIDGE WELLS SAND	Fine buff sand, much of it compacted into soft sandstone or massive rock. Local clay beds.	Mainly on flanks & at western end of High Weald,
			HASTINGS BEDS — WADHURST CLAY	Clay & shale with thin beds of sandstone. Nodules of ironstone.	Exposed mainly in valleys of the High Weald.
			HASTINGS BEDS — ASHDOWN SAND	Variable sand & sand-rock with beds of silt & clay.	Exposed on highest ground near centre of High Weald. Extensive outcrop also on northern flank, brought up by Penshurst anticline.

G.E.H.

In a general way the surface rocks of the Weald and the London Basin are seen to form two complementary structural units. The first is a complex arch or *anticline* spanning the area between the Thames and the Channel coast but dying away westward in the gently folded Hampshire Chalk and eastward in the Boulonnais country of northern France. The *Weald*, using the name in its historical meaning, is really the inner part of this region where the Lower Cretaceous rocks appear at the surface of the ground. Geographers now usually include in the Wealden unit the whole of its surrounding rim of Chalk upland because the Chalk strata, inclined north and south away from the central axis, form so conspicuous an element in the anticlinal complex.

The second structural unit, the London Basin, is a broad trough or *syncline*. The form of the trough is clearly shown by the thick layer of the Chalk which is inclined from the high ground of the North Downs towards the Thames and passes beneath Central London at a depth of some 200 feet below ground. It rises again to the north of London to become the elevated range of the Chiltern Hills. Filling the centre of the syncline are the sands and clays of the older Tertiary (Eocene) series (Fig. 3).

Our general account of the country traversed in the excursions may conveniently be given in two parts, one dealing with the country south of the Thames, the other with the central and northern districts. It is clearly impossible to draw a precise boundary between two such complementary regions as the Weald and the London Basin. Roughly their frontier could be taken as the southern margin of the Eocene deposits, but this would be an irregular and inconvenient boundary for dividing the regional description. We may therefore use the Thames as the dividing line, bearing in mind that the parts of Surrey and Kent for some distance south of the river are physiographically part of the London Basin and do not properly belong to the Wealden region.

The Country South of the Thames

The disposition of the rocks of the Weald as we now see them, and the surface form of their exposed parts, cannot be reconciled with the notion of a uniform dome of strata uncapped by some simple process of erosion. On the evidence of numerous folds and faults observable all over the region, some of them profoundly affecting the morphology of large areas, we know that the structure of the uplifted mass could never have been that of a simple anticline. Moreover, there is much evidence to show that the erosion processes which have reduced the Weald to its present form, have been of varied character and long duration.

The main folding of the Weald took place about the middle of the Tertiary era—probably near the beginning of the period known to geologists as the Miocene. A long period of river erosion lasting through the rest of Miocene times then reduced the whole of the Weald to the condition of a *peneplain* lying little above the then sea-level. This land surface was later invaded by a Pliocene sea which, during its sojourn in the area, effected further planation around the outer margins of the Wealden area and across the London Basin. It is probable that the central parts of the Weald remained dry land during the Pliocene period, forming a long narrow island at the time of the maximum extension of the invading sea.

The present drainage system of the Weald, which has but half completed its cycle of erosion, was initiated on a newly uplifted surface consisting of the Pliocene sea-floor and the remains of the Miocene peneplain at slightly higher levels. This elevated surface has been almost wholly destroyed; it is represented today only by the widely separated summits of the highest hills (those which stand at altitudes of 600 feet or more above sea-level). The rest of the country has been eaten out by the post-Pliocene rivers into wide valleys and broad plains, a stage towards the production of a new peneplain.

The new lowland is naturally best developed on those rocks which offer least resistance to erosion: the Weald Clay, the Gault and the London Clay. The more resistant rocks, the sandstones and the Chalk, which alternate with these clays in the rock sequence, stand up as hill ranges above the general lowland level. They comprise the compact sandstones of the Hastings Beds, the sandstones of the Hythe Beds (Lower Greensand) and the Chalk, relatively resistant because permeable. The Hastings Beds form the hilly central core of the Weald, a wide oval-shaped area much dissected by the headstreams of the Wealden rivers whose valleys divide the mass into a complex series of ridges, the 'Forest

Ridges' as they have been aptly named. The hills of the Lower Greensand and the Chalk are aligned on each side of the central highland in two roughly parallel ranges. The inner one, that of the Greensand, is separated from the Forest Ridges by the wide vale of the Weald Clay, and from the outer rim of Chalk by the narrower vale of the Gault. The Chalk and Greensand ranges face the central Wealden area in *escarpments* of varying form and steepness, while their back-slopes or dip-slopes express the general tilting of the several rock sheets away from the central Wealden axis. These forms are clearly seen in almost any landscape in the outer Weald, and are shown in such transects as those of Figs. 20, 26 and 30. The Chalk escarpments of the North and South Downs, though varying in form from place to place and differing from one another in certain important respects, make a remarkably uniform wall round the Weald. They are fairly consistent in height (600 to 800 feet), and the only important breaks in their continuity are the imposing gaps through which the main Wealden rivers pass on their way to the sea. The Greensand hills have no such uniformity; they vary greatly in height and breadth, and in places the Greensand is no longer preserved as a hill feature.

In addition to these main hill ranges made by the more resistant rock layers, the lowlands of the Weald and neighbouring parts of the London Basin are relieved here and there by other upstanding features. There are, for example, local bands of sandstone and limestone within the mass of the Weald Clay. Where these have a surface outcrop there is inevitably a small hill feature. Again, where clays are overlain by gravels or sands the normal processes of erosion may be modified in an interesting way. The gravels, though unconsolidated and friable, may escape erosion because their permeability restricts surface drainage. They thus constitute a protective capping to the underlying clay. Around the margins of such cappings there is usually considerable erosion by springs, and locally this may result in the apparent anomaly of scarp formation in the clay mass. Examples of this kind of hill feature in the softer rocks are to be seen in the western end of the London Basin where the Bagshot Beds cover the London Clay, and also to the south-east of London where the Blackheath Pebble Beds form a relatively high plateau over the clays and sands of the Lower Eocene beds.

We have now given a very brief account of the Weald as a whole. It remains to describe in rather more detail the tract of country to be covered by the field excursions and to elaborate some points in the physical history of the Weald in the light of this more local study. The more or less parallel outcrops of the Cretaceous and Eocene rocks round the Weald are the basis of a clearly marked geographical zonation of the country, for the contrasting rock types determine the variety of relief, hydrology and soils in the region, and these in turn profoundly affect its pattern of natural life and human settlement. The area with which we are concerned can only be effectively described in terms of these physiographic zones. We may consider them in turn, working southward from the Thames towards the inner Weald.

I. THE EOCENE BELT

Through Surrey and West Kent the Eocene sands and clays occupy a belt of country some 8 miles wide, having its southern margin roughly parallel with the Thames along a line through Sutton, Croydon and Orpington. The complete succession of the Eocene strata up to and including the Bagshot Beds is best preserved in the western end of the London Basin; to the east the higher beds have been more extensively denuded and the lower members of the series are exposed over a correspondingly larger area of the surface. It is thus possible to divide the Eocene belt south of the Thames roughly into three sectors. The first, extending eastward to just beyond the Mole valley, comprises an extension of the Bagshot plateau country bordered by a London Clay lowland; here, at least over the predominantly high ground, the Bagshot Sands rest on the full thickness of the London Clay (300 to 400 feet). The middle sector of the Eocene belt, between the Mole and Croydon, is an area of generally lower relief over which the eroded surface of the London Clay is exposed. The eastern sector, between Croydon and the Darent valley, is that in which the 'Lower Tertiaries' (Blackheath, Woolwich and Thanet Beds) occupy most of the surface of the ground, the London Clay remaining only in separate outliers.

Of the western sector of the Eocene belt we are concerned with only a small portion, where the river Mole passes across its eastern end. Farther west, near Aldershot and Guildford, the Bagshot plateau is no less than 12 miles wide, but it narrows rapidly to the east of Guildford where it is cut through by the river Wey. The plateau is again severed by the Mole only 1½ miles farther east, thus isolating the flat-topped ridge of St George's Hill, Weybridge. A final segment of the Bagshot plateau is preserved in the highest parts of Oxshott Heath and Esher Common on the east side of the Mole valley. The Bagshot Beds which cap the London Clay over all this higher ground in north-west Surrey consist of predominantly fine quartzose sands. They give rise to light, dry soils which are difficult to make fertile. Hence most of the ground is occupied by heath and birch with quantities of planted coniferous timber.

The Bagshot Sands do not rest directly on the London Clay; there is a transition through 'passage beds' consisting of well-defined alternations of clay and sand about 50 feet in total thickness. These are the Claygate Beds, named from a place near Esher where they are exposed in brickworks. The Claygate Beds have a surface outcrop up to ¾ mile wide round the lower slopes of the Oxshott–Esher hills. They occur to the east and north of this district as scattered outliers on the London Clay but without the Bagshot Sands above them. Such outliers are situated at Claygate itself, Chessington, Richmond Park and Wimbledon Common. It is interesting that one other, far to the north-east, lies on high ground near the site of the Crystal Palace, one point in south London, therefore, where it is certain that the full thickness of the London Clay is present.

The middle sector of the Eocene belt extends from the Mole to beyond the Wandle valley, an area over which a great expanse of London Clay is exposed. Except for the high ground between Richmond and Wimbledon (up to 200 feet O.D.) it is a surface of low relief, intersected by small streams in shallow valleys. Large spreads of river gravel cover much of the lowest ground, not only along the margin of the Thames but over the floors of the chief tributary valleys. Where this cover is absent the surviving rural parts of the London Clay country (now diminished by the enormous expansion of suburban London) are largely pasture land with woody hedgerows characterized by a profusion of elms. In this country surface water is abundant in winter but fails in the summer months; its unreliability as a source of supply for domestic and agricultural purposes had in the past greatly restricted rural settlement.

Along the southern edge of this sector is the narrow outcrop of the Thanet Beds and the Woolwich and Reading Beds which separate the expanse of the London Clay from the rising ground of the Chalk. This line coincides very nearly with the spring-line of Chalk water.

The eastern sector of the Eocene country presents a new and conspicuous element in the stratigraphical sequence, the Black-heath Pebble Beds, coming between the Woolwich Beds and the London Clay. In north-west Kent the Blackheath Beds have an extensive outcrop, the London Clay being reduced to a number of broad *outliers* upon it. This part of the Eocene country rises to moderate elevations (200 to 300 feet, with the still higher London Clay mass of Shooters Hill near the Thames at 424 feet O.D.). Like the Bagshot Beds farther west, the pebbly sands of the Black-heath Beds give infertile soils which support modified forms of heath vegetation. This may be seen on the numerous areas of common land such as those of Bostall Heath, Hayes, Keston and Chislehurst Commons and the Addington Hills. The Thanet Sands and the Woolwich Beds continue their narrow outcrop along the southern margin of the mass from Croydon to Keston. In this sector, owing to the presence of the overlying pebble beds, there is a true escarpment along the Tertiary edge. This persists north-wards along the side of the Cray valley to the Thames at Erith.

Along the Thames valley from Erith, through Woolwich and Greenwich, the outcrops of the Lower Tertiary beds are to be seen above the Chalk, the latter being brought to the surface here by a local anticline coinciding roughly with the course of the river. The beds are well exposed in the classic section at Charlton and else-where along the right bank of the Thames. Within the heart of the West Kent mass the lowest Tertiary beds are again brought up by local anticlinal folds; they appear as *inliers* near Eltham and Chislehurst.

2. THE NORTH DOWNS

In West Kent and the eastern part of Surrey the Chalk outcrop is 6 to 7 miles wide, but west of Sutton it narrows suddenly, and from Ashtead is more gradually reduced in width until it becomes the attenuated ridge of the Hog's Back west of Guildford. The Chalk outcrop varies in form as well as in width, and on this basis we may consider a number of distinctive sectors of the range.

The sector of the Chalk between Croydon and the Darent stands higher than the country to the west. It contains also the highest summits along the whole of the crest line of the North Downs, Botley Hill, near Limpsfield, reaching about 875 feet O.D. We may consider the general form of the Chalk range in this and the neighbouring sectors in terms of their N–S cross-sections (Fig. 4). It displays a distinct and significant zonation. Its southern

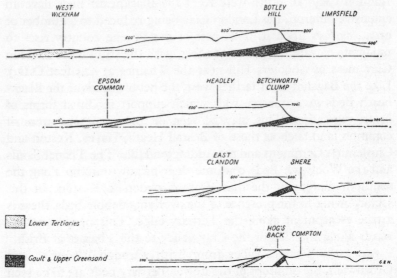

Fig. 4.   Sections of the North Downs in Surrey

face is an imposing escarpment rising steeply from the Gault vale, forming as it were the boundary wall of the Weald proper. The broad north-facing dip-slope of the mass is much more gently inclined, but it may be divided into three zones distinguished by difference in northerly gradient. The highest zone, lying immediately north of the scarp-crest, has an appreciable slope down to about the 650-foot contour. It is succeeded by a more nearly level surface, in places nearly 2 miles wide, grading down to between the 500- and 550-foot contours. At about that height there is another break of slope and the remainder of the Chalk surface falls more rapidly northward to about the 250-foot contour, which roughly marks the foot of the Tertiary scarp. These three zones of the dip-slope are not represented by continuous surfaces *along* the downs, for the whole of the Chalk upland is deeply dissected by systems of valleys running generally northward in the direction of the dip. These valleys, now streamless, are indeed the most conspicuous feature of the northern face of the downs; the true dip-slope surface is preserved only on the high ground between the valleys and around their heads.

The sector of the North Downs between the Coulsdon valley (Croydon) and the Mole gap differs in some important respects from that to the east of Croydon. There is a much smaller proportion of the whole surface in the highest zone (above the 650-foot contour); only the summit of Reigate Hill reaches 750 feet. The flatter zone, between 650 and 500 feet, is still present, but it narrows rapidly west of Headley Heath and almost bevels the scarp-crest in the triangular summit of Box Hill. With this narrowing of the high plateau westward the lower part of the dip-slope (below 500 feet) swings round so as to face north-west rather than north, and along the foot of this zone the edge of the Tertiary cover follows a line well below the 150-foot contour, that is more than 100 feet lower than the Chalk-Tertiary junction in the Croydon–West Kent sector. It may be noted that there is generally a difference in altitude of about 100 feet in *all* the features (except the 500–650-foot flat of the Chalk plateau) to the east and west respectively of a N–S line coinciding approximately with the London to Brighton road through Croydon; the difference in altitude is evident in the land surface of the Tertiary belt and also in the floor of the Gault vale to the south of the Chalk. At Box Hill the whole Chalk outcrop is only 4 miles wide. The westward narrowing towards this point is wholly at the expense of the high plateau elements, the lower dip-slope remaining fairly constant in width for some 10 miles from the east.

In the Chalk sector to the west of the Mole gap the westward narrowing of the outcrop is continued, until at Guildford it is no more than a mile wide. Reduction in width of outcrop is here associated with increasing northerly dip of the strata. At Ranmore, immediately west of the Mole, the Chalk ridge retains the three-fold division of its northern face—the upper and lower slopes separated by a more nearly level zone of the plateau—and, as

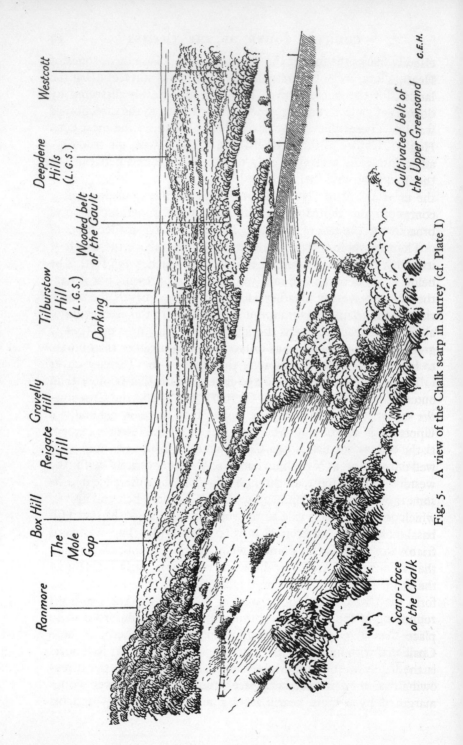

Ranmore — Box Hill — The Mole Gap — Reigate Hill — Gravelly Hill — Tilburstow Hill (L.G.S.) — Dorking — Wooded belt of the Gault — Deepdene Hills (L.G.S.) — Westcott

Scarp-face of the Chalk

Cultivated belt of the Upper Greensand

G.E.H.

Fig. 5. A view of the Chalk scarp in Surrey (cf. Plate I)

elsewhere, is trenched by dry valleys. Farther west, at Netley
Heath, the 600-foot flat comes to the scarp-crest, and beyond Newlands Corner this surface in turn disappears, the crest line of the
downs falling to below the 550-foot altitude. From this point westward the dip of the Chalk is even steeper. West of Guildford the
Hog's Back is a narrow ridge of Chalk rising but slightly above the
adjacent low ground of the Lower Greensand to the south and
the Tertiaries to the north. We have here an excellent example of
the effect of high dip, narrow outcrop and lowered altitude—a
contrast with, say, the Chalk mass of East Kent with its low dip,
broad outcrop and consistently higher elevation.

The most striking and uniform feature of the North Downs is
its bold, south-facing escarpment (Fig. 5). Viewed from the Gault
below it, or from high ground on the Greensand range to the south,
the Chalk escarpment gives the impression of a buttressed wall
rising from a broad and gently sloping glacis. Variations in the
altitude of its summit and of the floor of the vale at its foot are so
gradual that the whole Chalk range appears in its southern aspect
to have remarkable uniformity of height.

The lowest ground of the scarp vale normally coincides with the
outcrop of the Gault, but in places the clay extends part way up
the scarp-foot slope. Above the Gault the calcareous stone of the
Upper Greensand tends to stand out as a narrow shelf or bench
at the foot of the main scarp of the Chalk. This feature is not so
well developed in the North Downs as it is along the southern and
western margins of the Weald, but it is fairly conspicuous and of
some geographical importance in the sectors of the Chalk with
which we are concerned. The scarp-foot zone usually includes the
basal part of the Chalk itself. This is the *Chalk Marl*, a soft and
friable Chalk, devoid of flints and with a high clay content. Above
the Chalk Marl the rest of the Lower Chalk (the *Grey Chalk* of
the earlier geologists) and the whole of the Middle Chalk together
form the steep slope of the true scarp-face, a surface of smooth,
rounded buttresses alternating with shallow combes. At most
places along the range of the North Downs the base of the Upper
Chalk comes somewhere near the scarp-crest. The Upper Chalk
is the thickest of the three main divisions of the formation, but
owing to the northerly dip (Fig. 6) it thins out towards the southern
margin of the outcrop. It may be mentioned that the Upper Chalk

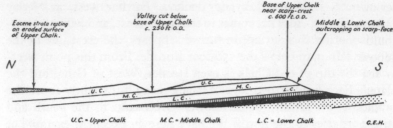

Fig. 6. Diagrammatic section showing the northerly dip of the Chalk

division is nearly pure calcium carbonate, though it includes the characteristic bands and nodules of flint which is such an important constituent of the Chalk formation.

Some general aspects of land use in the scarp zone may be noticed. The low ground of the Gault outcrop with its heavy, intractable soil is not greatly cultivated. It forms generally a belt of woodland and rough pasture. The heavy tree cover (predominantly oak) of the Gault belt makes it stand out in marked contrast with the relatively treeless ground of the scarp-face. Here the highly fertile soils of the Upper Greensand and Lower Chalk, or of the 'scarp drift' which in places lies over the lower slopes, give rise to a belt of cultivation. This in turn breaks sharply against the steep face of the Chalk scarp with its cover of natural vegetation—open sward with patches of Chalk scrub and occasional woods of yew and beech. The upward limit of cultivation along the scarp-face coincides generally with the line of an ancient trackway, the so-called Pilgrims' Way, one of the prehistoric highways of southern England (see p. 124 and cf. Pl. I).

Over the high plateau of the North Downs the Chalk is covered with a mantle of deposits to which the term *Clay-with-flints* has been rather loosely applied. True Clay-with-flints is a brown or red clay in which large numbers of broken but unworn flint nodules are embedded. This material includes the insoluble residue from the chemical wasting of chalk; it is often to be seen in section deeply pocketed or 'piped' into chalk surfaces which owe their irregularity to solution by percolating water. But the whole of the superficial deposits which lie on the surface of the Chalk upland cannot have originated in this way, for though an enormous amount of Upper Chalk has been removed from the flanks of the Weald by erosion, its low content of insoluble impurities could not provide residues in such quantity and thickness as we now see them. Much of the so-called Clay-with-flints contains flint pebbles which could only have been derived from the destruction of Tertiary deposits. It is not unlikely that much of the brown and red clay, to say nothing of the more loamy constituents of these mixed plateau deposits, is itself re-distributed Tertiary material.

Another and entirely different group of deposits is to be found on those more nearly level parts of the chalk plateau which lie at about the 600-foot altitude. We have already remarked on the existence of a flat at that level and its recurrence as a conspicuous element in the morphology of the Chalk upland. Wherever this feature has survived it carries deposits of sand or shingle, sometimes a considerable thickness but often only an attenuated remnant of a once thicker accumulation. This material is quite different from the Clay-with-flints. Locally it incorporates large quantities of flint in the form of unsorted shingle, comprising unworn or partly worn nodules and fragments, large rounded cobbles and small pebbles. In places fragments of chert from the Lower Greensand formation are present. The matrix of this assortment of stones is usually sandy, and there are sometimes beds of ferruginous sand without stones. The sands have mineral constituents by which they can be distinguished with certainty from sands of the Eocene series. Marine fossils obtained from these deposits were regarded as of Pliocene age (equivalent to that of the Red Crag of East Anglia), but recently reasons have been given for assigning them to the early Pleistocene. In order to facilitate references to the literature we will here retain the designation, Pliocene, for these high-level deposits. Their occurrence all along the North Downs, on the Chilterns and elsewhere in southern England, always on these nearly level surfaces consistently at the same altitude, has led to the conclusion that they are shore deposits resting on a wave-cut platform of the Chalk.

It is not difficult to imagine the general condition of the region when the Pliocene coast occupied a line somewhere near our present 700-foot contour (Fig. 7). The London Basin then contained more of its Eocene cover than has survived to the present day, but all of it submerged beneath the invading Pliocene sea. The Chalk of the North Downs at that time extended farther south over the Weald, whose lowland plains and vales had not then been

Fig. 7.   Map showing the Pliocene coastline in South-eastern England

carved out. The greater part of what is now the Weald would have
been a low island in the Pliocene sea, its highest summits on the
Hastings Beds and Lower Greensand being but a few hundred feet
above the then sea-level. Since the retreat of the sea sub-aerial
erosion has destroyed the exposed sea-bed across the London
Basin and much of the Eocene material that lay beneath it. Only
a few remains of the offshore platform of the Pliocene sea have
survived this long period of erosion; they are perched high on the
surface of the downs—small patches of shingle-covered plateau
around the heads and on the interfluves of deep valleys which now
score the Chalk dip-slope.

The valley systems of the Chalk downs are an important geographical feature, and their origin a matter of great interest. The
most cursory study of the map will show that the Chalk valleys,
though now streamless, fit perfectly into the natural drainage
pattern of the region; that is to say they form a tributary system
to the main rivers—the Thames or the Wealden rivers which join
it. Their general direction is down the dip-slope of the Chalk
and many of the valley systems are complete within the northern
face of the downs; others breach the scarp-crest making the so-
called 'wind gaps', suggesting that the valleys were initiated at a
time when the Chalk extended farther to the south. Altogether the
dry valleys effect a thorough dissection of the Chalk mass, such
that the true surfaces of the plateau and the lower dip-slope survive

only in patches either widely separated or connected by narrow necks of high ground.

There need be no mystery as to how this dissection was achieved; the valleys are clearly the work of eroding streams, and in some of them (e.g. that of the Wandle and some of the valleys of East Kent) weak streams still occupy their lower parts. The problem to consider is how the Chalk has come to lose its once active surface drainage. We cannot here examine all the evidence which led to the now generally accepted explanation of the disappearance of springs from the Chalk valleys and the connexion between this and other phenomena of Wealden denudation. The subject was thoroughly investigated by C. C. Fagg over 30 years ago.* His work should be of special interest to readers of this book in that his researches were carried out in the Chalk country of Surrey and West Kent. Briefly what Fagg has shown is that with the deepening of the Gault vale in conjunction with the northward recession of the escarpment there has been a lowering of the level of the scarp-foot springs by which underground water escapes from the Chalk; this in turn has lowered the 'water-table' or saturation level within the Chalk mass, so that the floors of the valleys on the dip-slope no longer lie in the saturated layers of the formation.

A highly pervious rock like the Chalk can only support surface streams if the rock itself is already saturated. Otherwise rain falling in the valleys and over the surrounding high ground percolates through the drier layers of chalk until it reaches a level where the fissures and other spaces are full of water, held up there by the impervious layer of Gault clay below. The underground reservoir of water (an intricate network of channels, large and small) is constantly being augmented by percolation, but at the same time it is being depleted by the emergence of water through springs along the margins of the Chalk outcrop, and also, it may be added, by the pumping of water from wells both in the Chalk country and through the Tertiary cover of the London Basin. The diagram (Fig. 8) shows how the margins of the outcrop have altered with progressive erosion, and how this has controlled the height of the water-table by lowering the spring lines. At a time when springs

* C. C. Fagg: 'The Recession of the Chalk Escarpment and the development of Chalk Valleys in the Regional Survey Area'. *Trans. Croydon Nat. Hist. & Sci. Soc.* vol. ix (1922), 93–112.

3

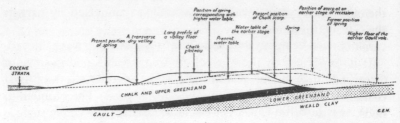

Fig. 8. The Chalk water-table in relation to the dry valleys and the escarpment (after C. C. Fagg)

emerged near the heads of the valleys the resultant streams were evidently not powerful enough to deepen their valleys at a rate equal to that of the subsidence of the water-table. The spring heads migrated down the valleys, doomed ultimately to expire, leaving on the Chalk surface a series of waterless valleys—an uncompleted work of land sculpture.

The great size and steepness of some of the Chalk valleys suggest that the earlier stages of their downcutting took place under conditions very different from those of more recent times. There were certainly periods during and between the arctic phases of the Ice Age when severe climatic conditions intensified erosion on the southern hill ranges. For the greater part of their length even the highest of the valleys had their origin on the uplifted floor of the Pliocene sea and have been cut down through a greater or less thickness of Pliocene and Eocene deposits before being incised in the underlying Chalk. When we speak of the 'stripping back' of the Tertiary cover from the surface of the Chalk we really mean that it has been removed in the ordinary course of the deepening and widening of the downland valleys. As the valleys were cut deeper into the underlying Chalk, their interfluves, capped by the Tertiary sands and clays, were wasted away by sub-aerial erosion until only a few outliers and attenuated remnants of the once continuous cover have survived.

3. THE LOWER GREENSAND COUNTRY

The sands and sandstones of the Lower Greensand formation emerge from beneath the Chalk and Gault to form a somewhat ragged fringe of hilly country round the Weald within the outer rampart of the downs. The stony lower layers of the series locally extend forward into the Weald to form a protective covering over the outer flanks of the thick mass of Weald Clay. Unlike the Chalk the Greensand range is very irregular and we may note some of its variations along the north-western margin of the Weald.

It is important first to consider the subdivision of the Lower Greensand formation, as the successive strata differ widely in character. The highest division of the formation, the Folkestone Beds, varying in thickness in this part of the region from 120 to 200 feet, is composed of coarse, clean-washed sand, usually yellow or gold coloured, and containing irregular concretions of hard, dark brown ironstone (known as Carstone). Even the unconsolidated sands of this division can form substantial hills, depending on the local circumstances of drainage. Generally, however, the surface of the Folkestone Beds shows subdued relief and forms a belt of low ground to the south of the Gault outcrop. The junction line between the sand and the clay is almost everywhere easy to observe, for the contrast between the soils of the two rocks is reflected in the vegetation and agriculture.

The Sandgate Beds, below the Folkestone sands, are insignificant in West Kent, but near Redhill they comprise up to 70 feet of soft sandstones in layers alternating with fuller's earth, a very fine-grained material with quite different physical properties from those of ordinary clay. Farther west the Sandgate Beds are loamy sands with little stone, but beyond Dorking their lower part consists of coarse sandstones, more or less calcareous, known as Bargate Stone. The Bargate outcrop is marked by highly fertile soils, a feature which has greatly influenced settlement along the north-western margin of the Weald.

The Hythe Beds in the eastern and middle parts of Kent consist of sandy limestone ('Kentish Ragstone') interstratified with softer sandstone or sand (known locally as 'hassock'). Between Maidstone and Sevenoaks the Rag has been quarried from early times for use as building stone. But an even more important feature of the Hythe Beds in this part of Kent is the fertility of its soils, the basis of the hop- and fruit-growing industry for which the region is famous. The Hythe Beds in West Kent and again in the western parts of Surrey are non-calcareous and give rise to poor soils largely left to support heath and woodland, much of it sadly neglected. The stone in these areas comprises sandstone and a hard siliceous stone known as 'chert'. Unlike the Kentish Rag these are indifferent building materials, used only locally for rough walling and road making. Between Redhill and Dorking the stony element in the Hythe Beds diminishes, the division being made up almost entirely of clean sand, generally finer than that of the Folkestone Beds. It is partly because of the absence of resistant stone that the Hythe Beds in this sector have failed to maintain any appreciable hill feature. To the west of Dorking, as in West Kent, the beds attain high altitudes over a broad but greatly dissected *cuesta*, its irregular crest line reaching heights of over 900 feet in places. The underlying Atherfield Clay, which in terms of stratigraphy properly belongs to the Lower Greensand series, may be regarded geographically as part of the mass of Weald Clay immediately below it.

The erosion of the Lower Greensand and of the Weald Clay, which it still in part covers and protects, is a process of which the history may be traced with some certainty, for it is still in operation and may be observed in the action of present-day streams and rivers. The Greensand ridge stands up between two belts of lowland occupied in part by streams flowing in the direction of the *strike* of the rocks. The streams are either E–W tributaries or parts of the trunks of the main Wealden rivers; they occupy respectively the lowest ground of the Weald Clay plain to the south of the Greensand hills and the floor of the outer vale of the Weald to the north of them. These strike streams receive the drainage of the Greensand upland, in the one case from its south-facing escarpment ('*obsequent*' drainage) and in the other by way of streams flowing down the northerly dip-slope. The drainage itself derives from springs or seepage near the junction of the Hythe Beds and the impervious Weald Clay, augmented in times of heavy precipitation by a considerable surface run-off. The Hythe Beds cover, rarely more than 200 feet in thickness over the higher parts of the upland, is greatly dissected by its drainage network. Some of the streams have cut through the sand and sandstone into the underlying clay. In valleys where this has happened, and also along the southern scarp-face, erosion of the slopes is accelerated by land-slipping. Penetration of the rocky layers of the Hythe Beds is inevitably succeeded by more rapid disintegration, for the exposed foundation of clay is readily eroded. A good example of the breaking up of the Hythe Beds cover is to be seen in the country between Dorking and Leith Hill (see pp. 108–9). This high ground, now extensively breached, adjoins the tract between Dorking and Reigate to the east in which the Greensand hill feature, whatever its former dimensions, has already been destroyed. A study of the maps of Surrey and West Kent will show the important part played by obsequent drainage (southward into the Weald Clay) in the denudation of the Greensand hills.

4. THE INNER WEALD

The Wealden rocks (the Weald Clay and the Hastings Beds) were laid down as sands and muds in a vast delta which extended over the area of present-day south-eastern England and northern France. The deposits contain the fossil remains of plants, terrestrial or semi-aquatic reptiles, fish and freshwater shells.

The upper division of the Wealden, the Weald Clay, includes strata over 1,000 feet in total thickness. These are predominantly clays, as the name implies, but there are among them local beds of sandstone and limestone. Where these harder beds appear at the surface they stand out in marked elevation above the general low level of the ground. In West Kent and East Surrey the clay belt or 'Low Weald' is from 6 to 8 miles in width, forming a broad plain between the Greensand hills and the elevated country of the Central or 'High' Weald. West of Horsham the plain encircles the diminished end of the central mass of sandstone and is continued along the southern side as part of the floor of the Vale of Sussex. Only in a few localities does the surface of the Weald Clay rise to summits above 250 feet, though along the northern margin of the outcrop it reaches 500 feet and more (over 700 feet at Leith Hill), where it forms a broad, gently sloping glacis to the Hythe Beds escarpment (Figs. 9, 26 and 30).

The Weald Clay lowland is covered by a *dendritic* drainage network. The streams receive water from the High Weald to the south and, as we have noted, from the broken fringe of Lower Greensand hills to the north; there is also a considerable surface run-off from the impervious clay itself. It is the erosive action of the streams which has reduced the surface of the Weald Clay to its present low level. Like other processes of planation, that of river action necessarily destroys most of the evidence of its own origin and early history. We can only conclude that the Wealden rivers

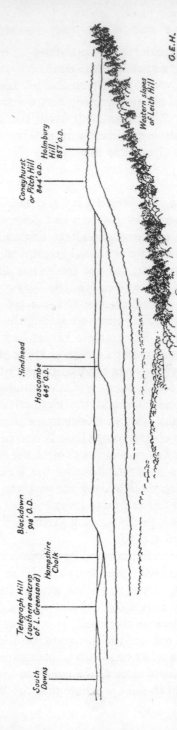

G.E.H.

Fig. 9.   Profiles of the Hythe Beds escarpment as seen in the view westward from Leith Hill

originated on a land surface much higher than that of the Weald Clay today—probably a surface constituted of Lower Greensand or even higher strata.

The High Weald is the name aptly used for the mass of the Hastings Beds which protrudes from the thick mantle of Weald Clay (Fig. 3), its fairly bold relief culminating in the irregular crest of the central watershed of the region. The Hastings Beds comprise two main sandstone layers, the Tunbridge Wells Sand and the Ashdown Sand, separated by the thick layer of the Wadhurst Clay. There are, however, subsidiary beds of clay in the sandstones and thin bands of stone in the clays. To add to the difficulty of studying this stratigraphical complex, the Hastings Beds are much disturbed by minor folds and faults (Fig. 33). These structures produce a mosaic of outcrops which is in places difficult to interpret. Nevertheless, the High Weald exhibits certain broad characteristics of landscape which are easily understood and which are reflected in the pattern of land use and settlement in this part of the region.

Generally the Tunbridge Wells sandstones, the highest division of the Hastings Beds, occupy the outer flanks of the mass adjacent to the Weald Clay, though they extend in places well towards the centre. The Ashdown Sands, the lowest division, has a broad outcrop over the highest ground (Ashdown Forest) in the west-central area, but is also brought to the surface near the northern margin by the Penshurst anticline (see pp. 168–9). The Wadhurst Clay is notable as containing the seams and nodules of ironstone which were worked as the basis of the famous Wealden iron industry.

The main watershed of the Weald, dividing the northern and southern river basins, follows an irregular crest-line from west to east through the heart of the Hastings Beds country, and on either side of it there is a deep and intricate dissection of the sandstone mass. On the part of the northern flank with which our excursions are concerned the tributary streams of the Medway travel long distances in valleys directed west to east; strike valleys are in fact dominant in the dissection of this part of the High Weald, so that the hill country towards the Kent–Sussex border is broadly a succession of east–west ridges, broken by the short northerly passages of the drainage system (cf. Fig. 14, p. 34).

A Note on the Wealden Rivers, with special reference to the River Mole

Frequent reference has been made in the preceding pages to phenomena of drainage and erosion. We may here with advantage sketch the history of the denudation of the Weald and adjacent parts of the London Basin, using particularly the evidence afforded by features of the Mole drainage, since a number of the excursions outlined in the book are devoted to the study of that river.*

The Mole, like the other rivers of the Weald, flowed originally across the surface of the land upraised by the Wealden folding (p. 7). During the succeeding Miocene period these rivers reduced the area to a peneplain. Parts of the peneplain were later invaded by the advancing Pliocene sea, which effected a more perfect planation and laid down deposits of sand and shingle. The old pattern of drainage was thus in part effaced, though the rivers doubtless continued in their original courses on those parts of the Miocene peneplain which had lain out of reach of the invading Pliocene sea (the 'Wealden Island', Fig. 7). As the sea retreated the Wealden rivers extended their courses northward across the exposed sea-floor, though not necessarily in courses following the exact lines of their pre-Pliocene forerunners. The upraising of the Pliocene sea-floor thus marks the initiation of an entirely new cycle of erosion to which the whole of the present dissection of the land must be ascribed.

The Wealden rivers and their tributaries now flow on extensive lowlands about 600 feet lower in general level than the highest parts of the land surface on which the drainage systems of the earlier cycle flowed. This new surface at the lower level is the outcome of the erosion and removal of a vast volume of soft rock material (mostly sand and clay) of which the land mass is largely composed. Only where more resistant elements (Chalk and sandstone) are present have any relics of the original upland survived, and only in the Chalk itself are the river valleys so well preserved

* For earlier accounts of the features of the Mole see: (1) Wooldridge, S. W., and Bull, A. J.: 'The Geo-morphology of the Mole gap', *Proc. Geol. Assoc.* vol. 36 (1925), p. 1; and (2) Green, J. F. N., and others: 'The river Mole, its physiography and superficial deposits', *Proc. Geol. Assoc.* vol. 45 (1934), p. 35.

that their sides register all the stages in the long process of downcutting.

The rock formations in the Wealden river basins are disposed, as we have seen, in east-to-west bands. The general direction of drainage is at right angles to these, and the form of the main valleys varies with the resistance of the rock elements in the succession. Variation in the resistance of the rocks has not affected the uniform downcutting of the rivers. Differential erosion (the destruction of rock materials at different rates according to their relative resistance) shows itself only in the greater *lateral* wasting of the less permeable rocks, that is in the greater degree of valley widening, and in the extension along their outcrops of large tributary systems whose streams in turn effect a great amount of lateral erosion. In this way the familiar scarpland sequence of the Wealden land surface has been evolved.

In the Mole basin (Fig. 10) there are representative sectors of the three lowland zones of the sequence, the Weald Clay plain, the Vale of Holmesdale and the London Clay plain with its remnants of low plateaux. Alternating with them are the scarped hill ranges of the Lower Greensand and the North Downs Chalk. The main stream of the Mole and some of its upper tributaries have their source on the northern flanks of the elevated central mass of the Weald (Hastings Beds). A large part of the Mole catchment lies on the Weald Clay plain, a surface of greatly reduced relief traversed by a network of Mole tributaries. The relation between the Weald Clay and the Lower Greensand in this sector of the Weald has already been discussed (see p. 22).

The lowland of the Vale of Holmesdale, formed on the outcrops of the Gault and the Folkestone Beds, is seen in its typical development west of Dorking. To the east of Dorking, as we have seen, this belt of lowland is now practically contiguous with the plain of the Weald Clay owing to the reduction of the former Greensand feature.

The Chalk mass stands across the Mole basin from west to east like a broad, high wall, the river passing through it in a comparatively narrow defile, the well-known Mole Gap. The Chalk has successfully resisted reduction to the general lowland level except along the relatively narrow strip of the valley floor. The Chalk on either side of the gap, although deeply scored by valleys (now

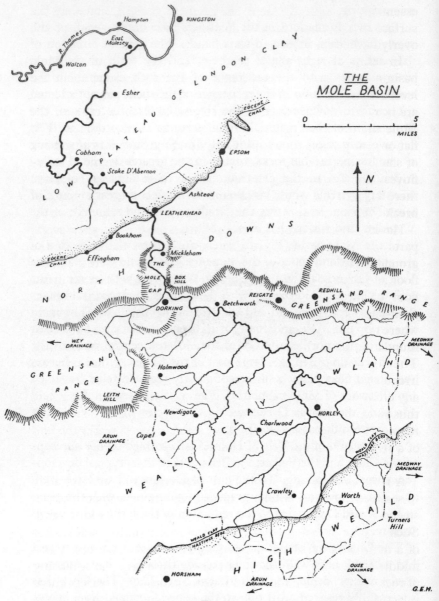

THE
MOLE BASIN

0   5
MILES

N

R. Thames

Hampton   KINGSTON
East
Molesey
Walton

Esher

Cobham   EPSOM
Stoke D'Abernon   EOCENE
                          CHALK
Ashtead
LEATHERHEAD

Bookham   Mickleham
                 THE
EOCENE   MOLE   BOX
CHALK   GAP   HILL
Effingham

DORKING   REDHILL
                 Betchworth   REIGATE
                 GREENSAND RANGE

WEY
DRAINAGE   MEDWAY
                              DRAINAGE

GREENSAND   Holmwood
RANGE

LEITH
HILL   Newdigate   CLAY   HORLEY
                 Charlwood
ARUN
DRAINAGE   Capel   WEALD CLAY
                                    HASTINGS BEDS
                 LOWLAND   MEDWAY
                                    DRAINAGE
WEALD

                 Crawley   Worth

                 CLAY   Turners
                 HASTINGS BEDS Hill
WEALD CLAY

HORSHAM   HIGH   WEALD
ARUN   OUSE
DRAINAGE   DRAINAGE

                                    G.E.H.

Fig. 10

LOW PLATEAU OF LONDON CLAY

NORTH   DOWNS

streamless), has no extensive low-lying surfaces; it is everywhere essentially an upland. Along its northern margin, however, the surface of the Chalk declines gradually towards the edge of the overlying Eocene sands and clays.

In terms of relief the Eocene or 'Tertiary' belt of the Mole basin may be described as a greatly dissected plateau at about the level of 200 feet O.D. The flat summits at or a little above this level are now separated by tracts of lower lying land, including near the Mole and the Thames considerable portions of river terraces. The flat or gently sloping lowland of the London Clay bears a network of shallow stream valleys widely separated by low, rounded interfluves. The Tertiary area has few striking relief features. Here and there a length of degraded escarpment and occasionally a river cliff break the monotony of the gently rolling London Clay country.

Having described briefly the physical features of the several parts of the Mole basin we may now consider the form of the ground adjacent to the river itself—such remains as there are of the floor and sides of the main river valley. We shall see that the broad floor of the valley comprises more elements than the present *flood-plain*. The latter is a belt of nearly level land, present everywhere on either or both sides of the river. It is the land subject to inundation at times when the river overflows its normal channel. The flood-plain is flanked here and there by broad, flat terraces, irregular in shape but conforming to a definite system of levels. In any cross-section of the valley (Fig. 22) the whole valley floor may thus resemble a series of shallow steps. The terraces are surviving remnants of older valley floors. Each of their levels marks the end of a stage in the deepening of the valley, *for downcutting has been intermittent*.

A river at work on a stable land mass tends to *grade* its valley to sea-level (or to the level of a major river) along a smooth curve, steepest at the head of the river and almost level at its lower end. Such a curve or *long profile* is the result of the mutual adjustment of a number of variables—vertical downcutting in the upper and middle sections of the valley, lateral *corrasion* and the spreading of rock-waste in the middle and lower sections. The perfect curve is actually never attained because erosion and deposition never quite cease, and run-off is subject to great variation in quantity. Moreover, the grading of the whole river to a fixed base-level would depend on a stability of land and sea which is not in practice sufficiently long sustained. A change in the relative level of land and sea will at once affect the conditions of grading. Thus, a land movement causing the river basin to tilt towards its outlet will affect all parts of the valley simultaneously and the whole curve will begin adjustment to the new overall gradient. If instead the uplift is of the same vertical amount over the whole basin re-grading will begin at the mouth of the river where the discharge falls to the new base-level. From this point a cut-back will begin to travel up the valley, represented by a new and independent curve breaking abruptly into the older one and extending at its expense farther along the profile of the valley. A further uplift of the land (or the equivalent fall of sea-level, as the case may be) would initiate another cutback and introduce a third curve of grade at the lower end of the long profile, and so on. Such a series of changes of base-level during the history of a river will therefore be revealed if the long profile of the valley is plotted and found to be a composite curve with a node (*knick-point*) marking the point of advance of each successive cut-back.

With the downcutting of each part of the valley another flood-plain will eventually be established at the new gradient. A flood-plain is the outcome of lateral corrasion by the river as it meanders in its course together with the spreading of a sheet of *alluvial* material at the level of flood water. Every new flood-plain occupies the bottom of a trench cut in the former flood-plain, parts of the latter remaining as a terrace. Above each knick-point the surface which has become a terrace in the downstream part of the valley remains the functional flood-plain of the river. So each terrace of a river valley, if followed along its own long-profile, will sooner or later grade into an upstream sector of the contemporary flood-plain. The relation between flood-plain and terraces is illustrated diagrammatically in Fig. 11.

The Mole valley presents a terrace sequence which tells much of the story of post-Pliocene denudation in the South-East. No other Wealden river displays the complete sequence so well. In the middle and lower sectors of all the other rivers (except the Wey) the younger terraces are buried beneath an accumulation of estuarine *alluvium* deposited in the valleys as sea-level has risen during the last few millennia (see p. 142). The Thames itself has

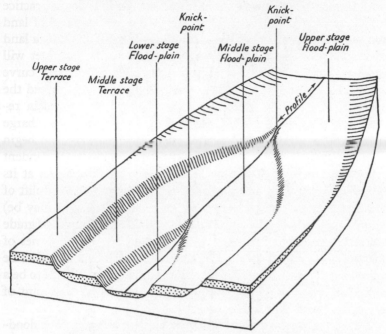

Fig. 11. Block diagram illustrating the flood-plains and terraces in a
river valley of composite profile

suffered this maritime invasion as far upstream as London. The
Mole and the Wey, which discharge into the Thames above London, have thus not yet been affected by the rise in sea-level. These
rivers are still grading down to their points of confluence with
the Thames, not, like the Medway, for example, or the southern
rivers of the Weald, to a new sea-level far inland along their
valleys. In number of stages and vertical spacing the Mole terraces appear to correspond with the well-known sequence in the
valley of the parent river Thames. A possible correlation of stages
in the two valleys is shown diagrammatically in Fig. 12. It should
be emphasized that the well-defined terrace sequence to be observed
in the Mole valley records only the later stages of downcutting.
There is evidence of an earlier Mole valley with parts of its broad
floor surviving on the high ground (400 feet O.D.) of Mickleham
Downs and Norbury Park (Fig. 13). Within this valley the steep-
sided trench of the present Chalk gap was cut. This stage of downcutting is registered by lines of cliffs, now much degraded, standing

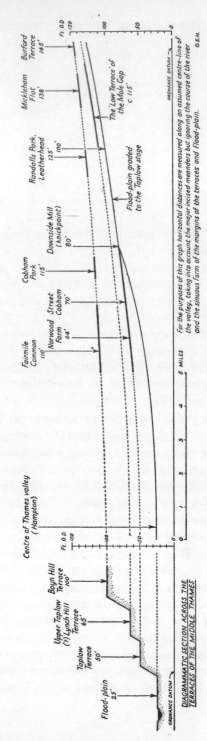

Fig. 12. Long profiles showing a possible correlation of the Mole terraces with those of the Thames

For the purposes of this graph horizontal distances are measured along an assumed centre-line of the valley, taking into account the major incised meanders but ignoring the course of the river and the sinuous form of the margins of the terraces and Flood-plain.

G.E.H.

Labels on Mole profile (upper):

Fairmile Common 110'
Norwood Farm 64'
Street Cobham 70'
Cobham Park 115'
Downside Mill (knickpoint) 80'
Randolls Park, Leatherhead 125' 100'
Mickleham Flat 138'
Burford Terrace 14·5'

The 'Low Terrace' of the Mole Gap c 115'

Flood-plain graded to the Taplow stage

ORDNANCE DATUM

Ft. O.D. 150 100 50 0

5 4 3 2 1 0 MILES

Thames profile (lower left):

Centre of Thames valley (Hampton)

Ft. O.D. 150 100 50

ORDNANCE DATUM

Boyn Hill Terrace 100'
Upper Taplow (?) Lynch Hill Terrace 65'
Taplow Terrace 50'
Flood-plain 25'

DIAGRAMMATIC SECTION ACROSS THE
TERRACES OF THE MIDDLE THAMES

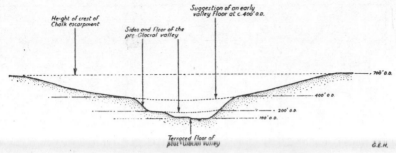

Fig. 13.   Diagrammatic section across the Mole gap

high above the shallow terraces of the valley bottom and breached by the openings of the now dry tributary valleys. Some 200 feet of vertical erosion is represented here, for the stage ended with the establishment of a floor at about the 200-foot level, a few small relics of which may be seen between Dorking and Mickleham. The 200-foot flat (grading down from about 230 feet in the Low Weald) is widely represented over the present-day lowlands; it forms the summits of many of the hills within the London Basin and represents a plain formed by river action early in Pleistocene time, before the widespread advance of ice into the region north of the Thames. The terraced floor of the Mole which lies wholly below the 200-foot plane is therefore to be regarded as the work of down-cutting during the later stages and after the Glacial Period.

In the north-western quarter of the Weald drainage is concentrated on four main rivers, Wey, Mole, Darent and Medway, each with its gap through the North Downs. The Wealden catchment areas of these rivers differ greatly in size and form; in the pattern of their tributary networks is to be read the story of contest and capture. Some episodes in their history will be discussed later in terms of local detail, but we may here remark that the Medway, by the activity of its obsequent affluents, originating in the Lower Greensand and now in some cases reaching back to the Chalk, has clearly beheaded the Darent, depriving that river of all the catchment it may have had in the Inner Weald. Even the more distant Mole has yielded some territory to the powerful Medway, while both the Mole and the Wey have lost parts of their former catchments to the south-flowing Arun, whose headstreams have greatly displaced the central watershed of the Weald (Fig. 14).

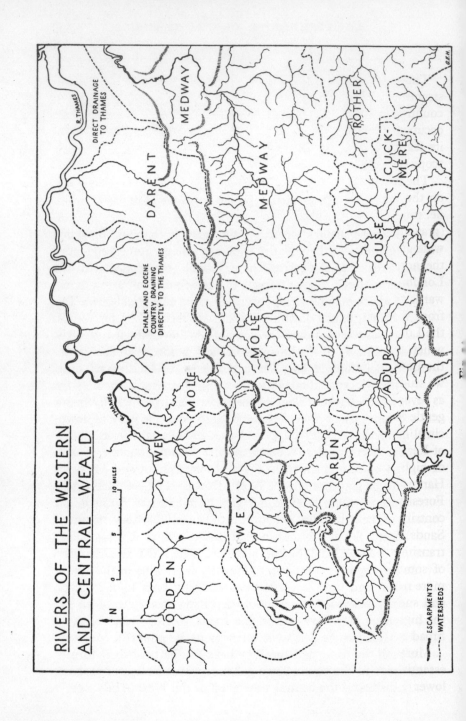

RIVERS OF THE WESTERN
AND CENTRAL WEALD

N

0   5   10 MILES

DIRECT DRAINAGE TO THAMES

CHALK AND EOCENE
COUNTRY DRAINING
DIRECTLY TO THE THAMES

R. THAMES

R. THAMES

DARENT

MEDWAY

MEDWAY

ROTHER

CUCK-MERE

OUSE

MOLE

WEY

MOLE

WEY

ADUR

ARUN

LODDEN

         ESCARPMENTS
- - - - WATERSHEDS

The Country North of the Thames

Though the country north of London is of very simple geological structure the evolution of its land forms has been complex and the country also bears the impress of a long and varied human occupancy. While, therefore, it is in some respects less striking in its features than the northern Wealden margins it offers ample scope for geographical field work.

The essential features in the build of the country are seen clearly on the 1-inch geological maps. Between the Brent and the Lea, i.e. roughly from Ealing to Hackney, the main belt of valley drifts (gravel and brickearth) in the Thames valley is about three miles wide and lies wholly within the built-up area of London. Beyond the northern edge of this belt the essential country rock is the London Clay which forms the greater part of the surface northwards to the line of the so-called 'Tertiary escarpment' running from Watford via Hatfield to Hertford. The general inclination of the London Clay, the underlying Reading Beds, and the Chalk on which they rest is of course southwards towards the main axis of the London Basin, but minor folding of the strata is made clear if we study the form of the Chalk surface beneath its Tertiary cover as revealed in the numerous wells and borings (cf. Fig. 34). This gentle folding has little direct influence on the surface; slight anticlinal bending of the strata has enabled erosion to open up inliers of Reading Beds near Pinner and Cuffley, while the broken ridge of high ground south of the Brent from Hanger Hill, Ealing to Hampstead and Highgate, continued beyond the Lea in the Epping Forest ridge, coincides roughly with a gentle syncline which has contributed to preserving outliers of Claygate Beds and Bagshot Sands along this line. The former, which are loamy 'passage beds' transitional between the London Clay and the Bagshot Sands, are of some geographical importance in giving a much lighter and more readily cultivable soil than the main mass of the London Clay and supporting a rather different woodland flora. They cap also the high ground westwards from Barnet to Stanmore and form a broad outcrop in the northern part of Epping Forest.

More important than this minor folding is the structural feature, essentially a N–S *monocline*, which has determined the form of the lower Lea valley north of Tottenham. The valley is the most

4

striking physical feature in the Tertiary country north of London. Its long gentle western slope is covered with valley gravel and brickearth but the eastern slope rises steeply to the heights of Epping Forest (Fig. 36). It is clear that the valley has steadily worked eastwards during its successive stages of downcutting and the immediate cause of this has been the easterly dip of the strata along this line.

The Reading Beds appear from beneath the main mass of the London Clay in a narrow sinuous outcrop from Moor Park, Rickmansworth to the neighbourhood of Hertford. The beds comprise pale coloured sands, brightly mottled clays and occasional beds of black flint pebbles. They rarely attain 50 feet in thickness and are only locally conspicuous in landscape or land use. Owing to a wide spread of glacial drift little is seen of the underlying Chalk immediately north of the Tertiary escarpment but beyond the drift belt it forms the broad dip-slope of the Chiltern Hills, scored by numerous dry valleys and by the wider trenches of the headstreams of the Lea and Colne basins. Locally, as at Ayot, near Welwyn, outliers of the Tertiary strata (Reading Beds and London Clay) rise in isolated hills above the Chiltern dip-slope, testimony to the fact that the Tertiary cover once extended far beyond its present main outcrop.

From these facts concerning the 'solid geology' of the area we can draw certain very broad conclusions as to its physical history. After the accumulation of the Tertiary (Eocene) strata on delta flats and in shallow seas covering the greater part of south-east England, the district was uplifted above the sea with accompanying folding, and the work of erosion began. The rivers of the district co-operating with general atmospheric wastage have stripped the Tertiary cover from the bordering Chalk uplands and removed the upper parts of the cover itself in the areas nearer London (see p. 10). The full thickness of the London Clay is 300–400 feet, but this is only preserved beneath the rare and scattered outliers of Bagshot Sands (Harrow, Hampstead, Highgate, High Beech, etc.).

To make clear the stages by which this great denudation has been accomplished we must take account of the various drift or superficial deposits which rest locally on the Chalk and the Tertiary beds. Leaving aside the valley drifts which margin the existing streams, the chief categories of drift recognized by the Geological Survey are four in number, the Pebble Gravel, the Clay-with-flints and associated deposits of the higher parts of the Chalk country, the Chalky Boulder Clay deposited as ground moraine by an ice sheet, and the glacial sands and gravels, generally representing *outwash* in front of the ice and associated with the boulder clay.

Of these the oldest is the Pebble Gravel which caps the highest summits of the Tertiary country, generally at an elevation of about 400 feet. Its distribution is clearly shown on the North London and Hertford sheets of the Geological Survey. The gravel is quite thin (3–10 feet) and the existing outliers are evidently remnants of a wide continuous sheet. It is composed chiefly of rounded flint pebbles from the Eocene beds and smaller white quartz pebbles derived from the Lower Greensand. At Hampstead and from Barnet north-eastwards towards Hertford it contains also small pieces of the characteristic chert which we have already met with in the Hythe Beds (Lower Greensand) of the Dorking district. We need not here pursue at length the long controversies in which geologists have engaged concerning the age and origin of this deposit. It has been regarded alternatively as a marine shingle or as an early river or glacial gravel and assigned either to late Tertiary (Pliocene) times or to an early stage of the succeeding Ice Age. We shall treat it here as an early Pleistocene deposit and agree that, in large part, it may well be a marine shingle marking the floor of a shallow sea, yet perhaps the most interesting and significant feature of the Pebble Gravel is the occurrence in narrow belts within it of Lower Greensand chert. This can only have come from the Weald and must have been introduced by rivers. The distribution of the chert gives an indication of the course of these rivers and indirectly therefore of the early ancestor of the Thames to which they must have been tributary. We shall find the chert on the high points of Hampstead Heath overlooking the present Thames valley. Clearly that valley cannot have existed when the chert pebbles were brought to the hill-top; it has been excavated since. Further, the river which brought the chert, probably an ancestor of the river Mole, flowed on northwards to the neighbourhood of Hertford and must have joined the ancestor of the Thames in this neighbourhood (Fig. 15). The Pebble Gravel thus gives us evidence that the early Thames (before the Ice Age)

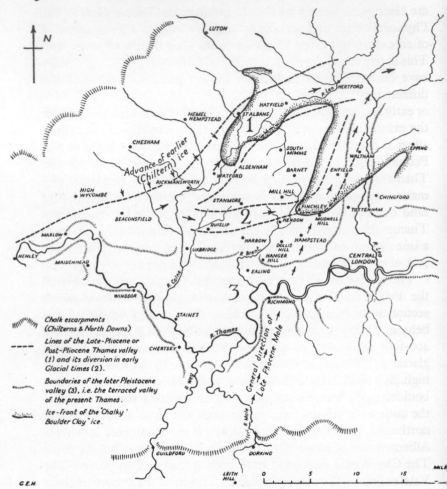

Fig. 15. Successive courses of the Thames during and after the Ice Age

followed a line far north of its present valley. It must have taken
this line when the shallow sea floor of the Pebble Gravel stage was
raised into land and its southern tributaries flowed from the Weald
across the site of the present Thames valley. This implies that the
Pebble Gravel includes two sets of deposits, the marine shingle
and the slightly younger river gravels formed of reconstructed
river gravel with the addition of Wealden debris.

Though some of the details of the story at this stage are obscure
and may never be resolved, certain main facts stand out clearly and

are essential to the understanding of the North London country. Physiographically the Pebble Gravel marks the surviving portions of an extensive though much dissected plateau at about 400 feet. This is the summit plain of the area and all the existing land forms have been sculptured during or since its uplift. It makes little difference whether we regard this old hill-top surface as Pliocene or early Pleistocene in date; it affords us a datum plane below which the existing valleys have been carved. Similarly it does not greatly affect the general argument whether we regard the whole of the Pebble Gravel as a sheet of river gravel deposited by the ancient Thames and its tributaries or whether we treat the main sheet as a marine deposit, invoking river action only when Lower Greensand chert is present. In either case it is certain that the earliest Thames of which we have any tangible geological evidence followed a line far to the north of London and has since shifted its line to that of the present Thames valley (Fig. 15).

The glacial deposits of the area cover a much wider expanse than the Pebble Gravel but show a more restricted distribution. A section from Hampstead to St Albans (Fig. 16) shows two main belts of glacial drift lying in broad depressions excavated in the 400-foot plateau. The more southerly drift belt comprises the glacial gravels, locally capped by boulder clay, which cover the high ground (200–300 feet) west of Enfield, the triangular mass of boulder clay which extends from Muswell Hill to Whetstone and the outliers of gravel at Hendon, Dollis Hill and Hanger Hill. The northerly drift belt, some 5 miles broad, occupies the Vale of St Albans, and its continuations, north of the Tertiary escarpment. The Chalky Boulder Clay is widely distributed on the floor of the Vale as far west as Aldenham; it rests on gravels which locally contain one or more layers of boulder clay.

It is clear that the ice which deposited the boulder clay advanced from the north-east, for in E. Herts and N. Essex the boulder clay sheet is almost continuous and, further, it extends in an unbroken expanse across E. Anglia. The ice sheet which deposited this boulder clay, over-riding the Chalk escarpment east of Hitchin, descended the Chalk dip-slope and, on encountering the high ground of the Tertiary country, the dissected 400-foot plateau, it sent one glacier-like lobe south-westwards along the Vale of St Albans to Aldenham and another to Finchley along the wide

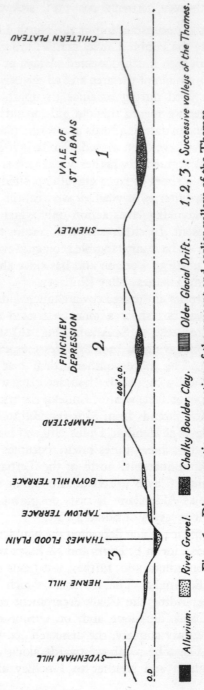

CHILTERN PLATEAU

VALE OF ST ALBANS

1

SHENLEY

FINCHLEY DEPRESSION

2

400' O.D.

HAMPSTEAD

BOYN HILL TERRACE

TAPLOW TERRACE

THAMES FLOOD PLAIN

3

HERNE HILL

SYDENHAM HILL

O.D.

Fig. 16. Diagrammatic cross-section of the present and earlier valleys of the Thames

1, 2, 3 : Successive valleys of the Thames.

■ Older Glacial Drift.

▓ Chalky Boulder Clay.

▦ River Gravel.

▒ Alluvium.

depression which separates Hampstead from the hills round Mill Hill and Totteridge. On the high ground separating these two depressions the boulder clay occurs in local patches to greater heights but it is here unaccompanied by true glacial gravel. The essential feature is that in both cases the main mass of the glacial drift lies in pre-existing valleys; these valleys were excavated at an earlier date.

In seeking an explanation of these relationships evidence must be gathered from a much wider area and cannot be fully stated here. We must note further that although the Chalky Boulder Clay ice sheet was responsible for the greater part of the glacial drift cover of our area, there is evidence both locally and further afield of glacial drifts distinct from and much earlier than those of the Chalky Boulder Clay series. Though no Chalky Boulder Clay occurs west of Aldenham the general run of the northern drift belt is continued by a belt of gravels south-westwards past Beaconsfield, Marlow and Henley to the high flanks of Goring Gap. These gravels are at a much higher level than those of Chalky Boulder Clay series. Moreover they appear to be associated with a chalkless boulder clay of local derivation, the product of a small ice cap occupying parts of the Chiltern Hills. There is thus clear evidence of a 'Chiltern Drift' accumulated long before the advance of the Chalky Boulder Clay ice sheet.

The sequence of events deduced from a survey of the northern drift belt as a whole is briefly as follows (Fig. 15). At an early stage of the Ice Age the Thames followed a line from Goring Gap northwards to Rickmansworth and it probably continued along the line of the present Vale of St Albans, though flowing at a higher level than the present floor of the Vale. In the west it deposited gravels derived from the outwash of melting ice lying on and north of the Chiltern Hills. Its north-easterly course through the Vale of St Albans was later interrupted by the advance of the Chiltern ice and it was deflected southwards so as to cross Middlesex with resulting excavation of the broad trough of the Finchley depression. Despite this diversion it is clear that a tributary stream became re-established on its old line in the Vale of St Albans, for the floor of the Vale was considerably lowered before the advance of the Chalky Boulder Clay ice. When this took place both the old St Albans route and the later loopway through Finchley were plugged with drift and the Thames was diverted to its present line through London. The lower Colne valley was initiated on the line of the outwash route from the Aldenham ice lobe while the Brent valley similarly marks the outwash route of the Finchley ice lobe. The lower Lea valley is the descendant, reversed in direction of flow, of the eastern part of the Middlesex loopway; its subsequent steady eastwards shift under the control of geological structure has already been noted. The existing drainage pattern is thus a legacy of the Chalky Boulder Clay glaciation. All the valleys, including that of the present Lower Thames, have since been deepened in successive stages, marked by the terraces of the valley drifts which yield us the occasional skeletal remnants, and the more numerous flint implements of Early Palaeolithic man.

We have given this sketch of a very complex series of events in order to indicate the general physiographic history of the country traversed by the routes described below. In following these routes we shall see part of the evidence from which the sequence is deduced and many related details of interest, notably the diversion of minor valleys brought about by the Chalky Boulder Clay drift. We must emphasize, however, that a full study of the points at issue involves a much wider area of country and must be pursued in the papers to which reference is here given. This is better done after the selected routes have been traversed and considered as a whole. Meanwhile some of the leading physiographic features of the country north of London may thus be summarized. There are here, in fact, three distinct and successive valleys of the Thames (Fig. 15). The present valley, the third and latest, contains no glacial drift near London. Its floor is occupied by a succession of terrace gravels and by the recent (*Holocene*) alluvium. The great depression north of Hampstead is a section of an older valley occupied before the Chalky Boulder Clay glaciation and abandoned as a result of the advance of this ice into the valley from the north-east. The Vale of St Albans marks the line of a still earlier valley but the Thames never occupied the Vale in its present form. It was diverted from this line to the Finchley route by an earlier glaciation responsible for the 'Chiltern drift'; the ice appears to have been local in provenance, forming on the Chiltern Hills. The details of this earlier diversion remain obscure, but it is clear that thereafter drainage towards the north-east was re-established probably in the form of a stream tributary to the Thames where the latter resumed its old line in the neighbourhood of Hertford. This stream deepened and widened the Vale before the advance of the Chalky Boulder Clay ice so that it later afforded lodgment to the Aldenham ice lobe and its old floor became thickly covered with the resultant drifts.

II Vegetation and the Earlier Stages of Human Settlement

The geological and physiographic features of the country we have described form a coherent unity best understood by tracing the successive stages of development. It is more difficult to deal in similar terms with the 'cultural' or humanized landscape, and yet we must need attempt the same *genetic* method if we are to understand our country in any real sense. It is obvious that its life today is largely conditioned by and subsidiary to that of London. The areas studied in this book, lying within about 30 miles of London, maintain a *primary* population, depending directly on the land, which nowhere exceeds 30 per cent. and is often less than 20 per cent. of all the inhabitants. The *secondary* rural population—shopkeepers, doctors, teachers, etc. who serve the needs of the rest—generally number about half the primary element. Thus the third element—the *adventitious* population, living but not working in the country—constitute from a half to threequarters or more of the total, a fact which here clearly marks the penumbra of Greater London. This is a summary relevant to the interests of the sociologist or the economist and it has too its plainly geographical bearings. But we should be missing most of the essence and interest of the craft of the geographer if we let such considerations obscure the fact that the human patterns of our countryside have grown through long successive stages, that the present scene is full of legacies from the past and that much of the pattern seen on the ground or the map is of ancient establishment. We can best approach our task by considering briefly first the nature and evolution of the plant cover, and then the course of human settlement. We shall find that the two themes are closely related.

Vegetation

Perhaps the most important characteristic of our area during the early phases of its human occupancy was its heavily forested con-

dition. Here in south-east England the summer deciduous forest
of western and central Europe reached its fullest and most typical
development. The principal trees of the forests were oak and
beech, often growing together, but the oak attaining its greatest
growth and dominance on the clay lands, the beech dominating
the woodlands of the drier soils on the Chalk and parts of the
sandy formations. The oak does not flourish on the calcareous
soils of the Chalk, though it grows well on the Chalk plateau
wherever this carries a thick cover of Clay-with-flints. The beech
is tolerant of a greater range of base status of soil, but it avoids
permanently wet situations, particularly on the clays. It is therefore only on sandy and loamy soils where beech and oak together
find favourable conditions, and where, in places, they may have
been co-dominant in the primeval forest.

At the present day we can distinguish two main types of oakwood, one on the heavy clays and moist loams dominated by the
Common Oak (*Quercus robur*), the other on the drier sands
dominated by the Sessile or Durmast Oak (*Q. petraea*). In both
types there is a varied undergrowth comprising a 'layer' of subsidiary woody plants (shrubs and young trees) and a 'field layer'
of herbaceous plants variously adapted for life in the shade of the
tree foliage. Hazel is the shrub most commonly associated with the
Common Oak on moist soils, but it is replaced by hornbeam in
parts of the country around the northern half of London. Usually
the subsidiary trees and shrubs of the oakwoods are varied,
numbering 20 or more different species, some favouring the drier,
others the wetter situations. Where the shrub layer is found to
consist of one species almost exclusively, such as hazel or chestnut
(a tree introduced into Britain by man), it is almost certain that the
wood has been planted and not merely modified from an existing
natural wood.

Here it may be remarked that the divergence of our present-day
woods from the type of the primitive natural forest is largely due
to 'coppicing', a practice dating from mediaeval times. In coppiced
woods the small timber (shrubs and small trees) is cut down at
intervals of 10 to 15 years and allowed to grow again from the
stools. Hazel, chestnut, hornbeam, ash and birch provide the most
useful coppice timber, but many others of the native trees and
shrubs are treated in the same way. Until recent years coppice

wood had a variety of uses which made it an essential commodity in the rural areas. The traditional practice of coppicing does not involve the complete clearing of a wood; a number of trees, chiefly the oaks, are left to grow, and are extracted for heavy timber as they mature. These are the 'standard' trees which give the name 'coppice-with-standards' to the particular kind of woodland. The minimum allowance of standards is about 12 to the acre. Oaks which are so spaced adopt a spreading habit. Formerly the curved and angled branches of such trees were in much demand for ship building. The production of long, straight timber requires the trees to be grown with their crowns everywhere in contact ('close canopy'), the best results being obtained when the trees are all of the same age, that is artificially planted. When coppice wood was in greater demand than it is now many woods were grown without standards. The practice is still current to a limited extent in the culture of chestnut coppice on sands and loams for the production of fencing stakes.

Many coppiced woods are now neglected and overgrown, being used only as cover for game. In this condition they may revert to one or other of the primitive oakwood types, though it seems that the natural regeneration of some species of tree, not least the oak itself, is to a great extent inhibited by the depredations of small mammals (rabbits, squirrels, mice and voles). The tree seeds or seedlings are eaten by these animals, and the animals themselves are not sufficiently suppressed because man has so reduced the numbers of their natural enemies (the predatory birds and mammals) in the interests of game preservation.

The few genuine relics of natural oakwood in Britain are on the margins of the upland. They are poorly grown compared with the robust type of forest which once flourished on the lowland soils. To picture the natural oak forest on, say, the Low Weald or the London Clay country, we must imagine a profusion of oaks of varying age, some of great size, forming a more or less closed canopy shading an undergrowth of shrubs, briars, brambles and coarse herbs. The undergrowth would have occupied every space between a mesh of fallen trees and branches. To the early inhabitants of lowland Britain the oak forests were impenetrable and sinister. Their clearing or modification was the slow work of many centuries.

On the Chalk of southern England beech is the dominant tree, the oak being present only where the Chalk is overlain by non-calcareous deposits of considerable thickness. On the North Downs and the Chilterns such deposits (Clay-with-flints, etc.) occupy large areas, the weathered surface of the Chalk itself being exposed only on the scarps and valley-sides. On these slopes are to be found a scatter of old-established beechwoods and numerous patches of maturing woodland of beech and yew replacing the sheep pastures of former times. Beech forms a fairly simple plant community, as the dense shade of its foliage precludes the growth of all other plants except a few shade-enduring species. These include the yew, box, whitebeam and elder among the woody plants; mercury, sanicle, ivy, a few species of orchid and other flowers in the field layer. The mixture of beech and yew is a common characteristic of the Chalk woodlands, and in places woods entirely of yew have become established on the downland slopes (cf. Pl. I).

The vegetation of the Chalk lands is of particular interest in the examples it offers of the process shown as 'succession'. Succession is the change from any 'open' unstable form of plant cover (for example, the vegetation of abandoned agricultural land) to a form which has more abundant vegetable growth and greater stability as to its composition. Succession always tends towards the development of a plant community which by its bulk and its longevity gives the greatest rate of conversion and storage of energy consistent with the conditions of climate and soil of the site. Such a community is called the 'climax' of the succession, and is commonly some kind of forest, though conditions may determine some lower order of climax.

Most of the steep slopes of the Chalk scarps and valley-sides are no longer grazed or cultivated. They support a natural cover of sward, scrub, or woodland which suffers little interference from the activities of agriculture or forestry. The tendency almost everywhere is for woody plants to invade the downland sward, giving rise to the scrub phase, and for the scrub in turn to give place to the woodland condition. The Chalk sward is rich in its variety of grasses and flowering herbs, some of which are peculiar to calcareous soils. The scrub also includes a number of species which either favour or easily tolerate the calcareous condition. Among these are the wayfaring tree, privet, juniper, yew, dogwood and spindle. The common hawthorn, the dog rose, elder, blackthorn and others, which, though also abundant in Chalk scrub and contributory to its characteristic appearance, are by no means confined to the Chalk lands. Chalk scrub, always an unstable plant community, varies greatly in composition according to its age and the condition of the land on which it originated. The process of its succession to the woodland condition is likewise variable. Thus, open juniper scrub on old sheepwalks may, with the cessation of grazing, become invaded by other shrubs among which yew becomes dominant, ultimately forming a closed yew wood. A mixed scrub containing much hawthorn, dogwood and privet may in time be invaded by birch, ash, yew and beech, a phase likely to lead to the beechwood climax. Once established beech is generally a successful competitor among the trees of the Chalk lands, but it is usually generated only in the proximity of parent trees, so that natural beechwood comes into being by the extension of existing woods rather than spontaneous growth over large areas of scrubland.

Other examples of succession may be studied in our area. Heathland, widespread on the various sandy soils, usually represents an arrested succession where tree growth has been prevented by factors such as exposure, recurrent fires, or a certain intensity of grazing. Heathland is dominated by the heathers, locally accompanied or replaced by bracken. Heathland grasses and flowers occupy the ground between the coarser growth of heather and bracken, and in places may form large areas of sward ('grass-heath'). Gorse and bramble frequently occur on heaths, either as scattered bushes or compact colonies. If the inhibiting factors are removed or ameliorated trees will invade heathland, birch being by far the commonest pioneer species. Birch, when well established, produces enough shade, shelter and leaf litter to create a 'woodland' environment favourable to the germination and growth of other trees. The succession may take any one of several forms according to the physical conditions of the site and the proximity of seed sources. Oak is perhaps the commonest partner of birch in woodland developed on heaths. Poor soil or lack of water, or a combination of circumstances, may prevent the oak from attaining complete dominance. Thus, instead of dry oakwood there may arise the familiar sub-climax known as 'oak-birch-heath', a community in which many elements of the heath flora are preserved and the birch is co-dominant with the somewhat stunted oak. Other trees enter the community in varying numbers, and among these holly, rowan, hazel and hawthorn are characteristic, the same species, in fact, which commonly constitute the shrub layer of the true dry oakwood.

On many of the southern heaths the Scots pine has become well established and in places assumes the role of forest dominant. The pine is thought not to be indigenous to the region. It is known to have been widely planted in the south during the seventeenth and eighteenth centuries and has since become naturalized. The self-sown pinewoods of the present day are therefore designated 'sub-spontaneous'. It is not unusual to see pine associated with oak, and even with beech, in the woodlands of the sandy soils, but each of these species has the capacity for sole dominance and therefore for determining a well-defined type of forest. When they are found mixed it is reasonable to suppose that the plant community is yet unstable and that succession will continue until one or other of the single-dominant climax forms is established.

Land with a permanently high water-table is characterized by plant communities and climax forms distinct from, yet in some cases related to, those we have described. Flood-plains of streams and the margins of other inland waters are usually maintained as pastures or hay meadows ('water meadows'), but if their drainage is neglected and their herbage left uncut or ungrazed they may develop scrub or woodland different from that of the better drained land. The climax of such wet sites is alder wood, a community which was no doubt more widespread in lowland Britain before the great expansion of agriculture and settlement in early historic times. As dominant tree the alder is usually associated with birch and ash at canopy level, and with the common sallow (a willow), buckthorn, blackthorn and other species in the shrub layer. Alder woods cover a rich field layer of moisture-loving plants ('hygrophytes'). In the better drained areas this stratum of the vegetation may resemble the field layer of the damp oakwood, but elsewhere will include many of the species characteristic of the yet unwooded swamps. Zonation of plant communities between dry land and open water often marks the progress of succession where hydrological conditions are changing, as when inland waters are drying up or becoming filled with silt (see p. 176).

Marshlands which have originated by the deposition of silt in 'drowned' valleys, where tidal water runs far up the rivers (see p. 142), carry vegetation which may show variations between the inland marsh communities (alder wood, reed swamp, etc.) and the distinctive salt-marsh communities of the estuaries and coasts. A great part of the estuarine marshland of southern and eastern England has been reclaimed by the artificial exclusion of tidal water, thus to provide drained pasture lands. These lands have quite a characteristic flora, but one which has been conditioned by centuries of grazing and the suppression of woody growth. We have little evidence to suggest what may have been the natural succession from salt marsh towards any sort of woody climax on these estuarine flats.

Earlier Stages of Human Settlement

We cannot here attempt any detailed account of the earlier stages of human occupancy in the area studied; the evidence from which the story is constructed must necessarily be drawn from a much wider field. Moreover, as we shall see, the actual imprint of prehistoric man in the northern parts of the Weald and the London Basin is very slight. One might walk observantly in these regions for a very long time without seeing evidence of any human past older than the Roman roads of which the map bears evidence. Yet if this were our conclusion it would be mistaken; our area lay, it is true, on the fringe of the settled lands of earlier times, but we shall not see the pattern of its own settlement in true perspective unless we sketch, if only briefly, the fuller record which these neighbouring regions afford.

The earliest traces of human life in the region are the flint implements and occasional fossil remains of Early Palaeolithic man. These are found chiefly in the gravels of the river terraces, notably those of the Thames and its tributaries. We can raise but little geography, in the proper sense, from the study of these scanty remains. Of settlement sites we know little: Palaeolithic man was a nomadic hunter. We are still, so to speak, within the confines of geology; the remains occur in stratified deposits, and since the earliest of these were laid down the face of the country has greatly changed, for the valleys have been deepened, the coastlines have

shifted and great climatic changes have occurred. The deposits of
the Boyn Hill terrace of the Thames and its equivalents (p. 40),
in which the massive flint hand axes and flake tools of Early
Palaeolithic man are common, were accumulated during one of the
milder intervals or 'interglacial periods' of the Ice Age. At a later
stage the cold returned in Europe; snowfields and glaciers again
occupied northern Britain while the south was tundra. Later
Palaeolithic man, the true 'cave man' of the world-famous localities of southern France and Spain, tended to move to more
southerly latitudes, though a few inhabited caves are known in
Britain, together with some 'open sites' which give evidence of a
group of men adapted to the hard conditions of the time, and
seeking their food by hunting the reindeer.

The succeeding *Mesolithic* phase dated about 6000 B.C. marks
the return of milder conditions succeeding the last glacial period.
Mesolithic man in southern England was still a hunter and his
presence is shown in the sandy country of the Weald by his
beautifully fashioned 'microlithic' flint implements. These are
generally surface finds in heathland, though a few occupied sites
with remains of fires etc. are known.

The first settled communities of southern England are of much
more recent date, though still prehistoric. Towards the end of the
third millennium B.C.—a period roughly contemporary with that
of the Old Testament patriarchs—the Neolithic people who built
the long barrows and the great stone tombs or megaliths travelled
by sea along the western coasts of Europe from the Western
Mediterranean lands and settled in our own western coastlands.
They entered also upon the higher Chalk country of Salisbury
Plain and the South Downs and other limestone areas. They have
left sufficient if scanty evidence of their life and economy. They
were primarily herdsmen, though locally they may have engaged
in a little cultivation. Their presence on the higher parts of such
an area as the South Downs presents something of a problem.
They had no means of clearing heavy forest and avoided the
forested lowlands. But the Chalk summits, even where bare of
Clay-with-flints cover, were certainly forested at an earlier time
and it is unlikely that the forest cover can at all rapidly have disappeared. The climate of the Neolithic times was becoming somewhat drier than that of the preceding period; this would have

5

tended to check forest growth and we can only conclude that the immigrant herdsmen made their first lodgements in local open glades or areas of lighter woodland and, by pasturing their animals and perhaps by burning, enlarged their grazing grounds.

The Neolithic stage was followed by the period of some 1,500 years assigned by archaeologists to the Bronze Age. During this long interval successive immigrant waves of people travelled to Britain from the European mainland. If we take a general view of the distribution of Bronze Age relics (including not only the bronze tools and weapons, but the characteristic pottery of the period and the round barrows in which the dead were buried) we see plain evidence of an increasing tendency to settle in the lowlands, at least on the lighter soils, though the clayland forests were still largely avoided. The high Chalk country still proved attractive however. On Salisbury Plain and the South Downs the Bronze Age newcomers met and mingled with their Neolithic predecessors and until late in the period the general style of life and economy seems to have differed little from that of the Megalith builders; the people were pastoralists rather than cultivators. In the latter part of the Bronze Age, however, more extensive cultivation of the lighter soils certainly began.

Here we may pause to note that the area with which we are particularly concerned—essentially the London District in the wider sense, was little adapted to the life of these early folk owing to the prevalence of Clayland forest and to its distance from the sea or from navigable rivers. The northern Weald yields little Neolithic evidence save scattered flint implements, though we must make exception of the notable group of megaliths in the Maidstone district (Coldrum, Kits Coty House, cf. p. 144). These lie close to the line of the scarp-foot track later known as the Pilgrims' Way (p. 124) and it is possible that this famous trackway like others of its kind originated at this time. There is also some evidence of Neolithic occupation of the Chiltern crest region between Princes Risboro' and the Dunstable Downs. Bronze Age evidence is somewhat fuller: there is evidence of settlement in the Medway and Wey basins and scattered relics indicate that the Weald was at least traversed if not settled at this date. An occasional round barrow is found in the Greensand country. It is clear, however, that the wide expanses of the Weald Clay, the London

Clay and the generally clay-covered high plateaux of the Chilterns and North Downs carried a forest cover difficult to penetrate and impossible to clear.*

In the succeeding Iron Age, which dates from about 500 B.C., a fundamental change began with the coming of iron tools and a more effective plough. It was then that the first real inroads on the forest were made and the cultivation of the rather heavier soils became possible.

The steady accumulation of evidence makes it clear that early Iron Age immigrants from the continental mainland made landings at many points on our eastern and southern coasts and their estuaries. Many habitation sites are known and the most conspicuous legacy of the time are the embanked 'hill-forts'. It is now clear that many of these were not temporary camps of refuge but permanently inhabited citadels serving as the capitals of tribal groups. Notable examples have been excavated on the South Downs and our present region presents three examples, not so well known, on the crest of the Greensand hills in Surrey, at Hascombe, Holmbury and Anstiebury (p. 114) as well as Loughton Camp in Epping Forest (p. 207).

Within a century of the coming of the Romans a further inroad of Iron Age people occurred in the South-East. Caesar found Kent and Hertfordshire densely settled by people from Belgic Gaul—the Aisne and Marne valleys. These Belgae mark a definitely higher level of civilization than their Iron Age predecessors. They came from a woodland country and were the first to introduce

* The subject of early forest clearance has lately been much discussed. Demonstration has shown that it is *possible* to fell a large tree by using only a stone axe or a bronze palstave, but it is a very slow and unrewarding process which could never have commended itself to prehistoric man as a means of clearing any area of well-grown woodland, an idea which probably never occurred to him. It would seem that clearance of forests took place not intentionally but as the result of feeding domesticated animals (goats, sheep and swine), first along the forest margins and later along certain favoured avenues. The animals would undoubtedly have destroyed the seeds and seedlings of the trees, thus arresting the process of natural regeneration. When the old trees died and decayed there would be no new woody growth to replace them. Their rotten remains would in time reach a condition in which they could be broken up bit by bit and removed, leaving clear space in the form of rough pasture. This at a later stage, according to the texture of the soil, might invite the use of the plough and the hoe, thus to become cultivated land.

to Britain an animal-drawn plough equipped with a coulter for
cutting the sod. For the first time it really became practicable to
cultivate heavy soils, and the Belgae established isolated farm-
houses which may have been directly ancestral in some cases to
the 'villas' of the Romans. A certain number of Belgic hill-forts
are known, but there is evidence at that date of the abandonment
of hill-top sites and the establishment of new towns in the
lowlands.

The further development of our region during the four centuries of Roman rule is indicated on the Ordnance Survey map
of Roman Britain which marks the towns of the period, the great
system of roads, the villas and other scattered finds indicating
permanent settlement. Of pre-Roman settlement on the site of
London there is little trace. Caesar's reconnaissance discovered
the Belgic capital in the great 'oppidum' near Wheathampstead.
Following his withdrawal the Belgae abandoned this site and
established their major settlement in what is now Prae Wood,
north-west of St Albans. The Roman city of Verulamium was the
lineal descendant of this settlement, in the neighbouring valley of
the Ver. The Prae Wood settlement had been the headquarters of
Belgic tribes of the Catuvellauni; Verulamium was its recognized
successor, a *municipium*, accorded rights of self-government in
accordance with the frequent Roman practice in Gaul. As such it
must have been, for a time at least, the virtual capital of south-
east England, and Roman London may well have arisen first as the
river-port of Verulamium. Upon it the Roman roads converged.
The course of Stane Street linking Chichester (Regnum) with
London can be traced on the ground we here study, crossing the
Mole, probably by a ford, at Burford Bridge, passing through the
grounds of Juniper Hall and then climbing over the high Chalk
country to Epsom. The first seed of Dorking may well have been
a posting stage on Stane Street, though the town is of later growth
and reveals no definite evidence of Roman antecedents. We may
similarly trace on our maps the course of the road from St Albans,
which crosses the Lea at Waterend and the Mimram at Welwyn.

Of the seven hundred and fifty odd villas known in lowland
Britain comparatively few occur in the London district. Several
have come to light in the country west of St Albans and there is
evidence that the country of the Holmesdale zone of the Weald

was locally farmed; villas occur, for example, at Titsey and at Farley Heath on the Leith Hill range. The villa in Ashtead Woods (p. 74) is of particular interest as lying in heavy London Clay country and giving evidence of the continued progress of the clearance and cultivation of the woodlands initiated by the Belgae.

The clearing of woodland and the spread of lowland cultivation during the long periods of prehistory was a slow spasmodic and piecemeal process. The earliest inhabited sites are on the hill-tops and high plateaux, their later successors as shown on the modern map are commonly in the valleys. There has been then, in a sense, a 'valleyward movement' of settlement. Yet this is, in some respects, an over-simplified and misleading way of stating the facts. Although we can trace, to some extent in the Bronze Age and certainly in the Iron Age, signs of progress in lowland settlement, and though some of the Roman villas stand in what must have been heavily forested country, the main attack on the forested lowlands and settlement in the valleys came only with the Anglo-Saxon settlement. In some parts of Southern England the contrast between prehistoric and later settlement areas is clear cut and unmistakable. On the Chalk of Hampshire and Wiltshire cultivation of the high ground, in the Iron Age manner, persisted throughout the Roman period. The villages of Belgic or other Iron Age folk, only slightly and locally touched by Roman influence, clustered on the plateaux, each with its accompanying area of small squarish fields. But the incoming Anglo-Saxons settled in the valleys and laid out their fields in a wholly different pattern. It is evidently less easy to establish this contrast in areas where the heavier soils had already been entered upon during the Iron Age, for the Anglo-Saxon pattern has there almost completely obliterated its predecessor.

It is this Anglo-Saxon pattern indeed which still provides the essential texture, in terms of human geography, of our modern maps in rural areas. We are not likely to overlook the heavy imprint of later centuries, in the growth of towns and communications, but it is easy, even near London, to over-estimate this. What we might call the 'village geography' of much of England is the direct legacy of the Anglo-Saxon settlement; most of our villages were established between about A.D. 500 and 1000, so that the essential settlement pattern is more than a thousand years old.

The evidence of archaeology and place-name study enables us to distinguish the areas first settled by the Anglo-Saxon peoples. The distribution of the burial grounds of the earlier 'pagan period' (A.D. 450–650), before the conversion to Christianity, gives a first clue. In general they are marked by no surface evidence like the prehistoric barrows, but are discovered only when their remains are turned up by the plough.

The Evidence of Place Names

The earliest of the place-names are those which in Old English had the suffix *ingas*, signifying originally a group of people whose name became attached to the place or small region they occupied. On the modern map such names generally end in *-ing* as in Dorking, Epping, etc. A good example from our area illustrating the significance and origin of such names is an eighth-century charter which speaks of the *regio* in the Middle Saxon territory occupied by the *Geddingas* : the name survives in Yeading.

The suffix *-ham*, as in Cobham, also marks the earlier crop of settlements, where it signifies village or homestead, for we have evidence that though freely used in the continental homeland (cf. German *heim*) it fell out of use after the earlier days of the settlement. There is, however, some risk of confusion with OE *hamm*, signifying meadow, generally low-lying stream-side meadow. Thus Brockham (p. 80) may be a name either in *-ham* or in *-hamm*, the earlier surviving form of the name giving no clue as to the choice. When the two early suffixes are combined in *-ingham*, as in Effingham, we are again probably dealing with one of the early settlements.

We can distinguish further a group of place-name suffixes which, while no precise date can be assigned to them, seem often to indicate generally later or secondary settlement. The common suffix *-ton* (OE *tun*) may sometimes be early but it certainly continued in use until the later stages of the settlement: there is evidence locally that a name in *-tūn* marked a later secondary settlement related to an earlier or primary village of the *-ham* group. Suffixes such as *-ley* (OE *leah*), clearing, open place in a wood; *-field* (OE *feld*), open country, land free from wood; *-don* (OE *dūn*), down, hill, mountain, often signify later settlement, since the name was originally given to a natural feature or a clearing and later transferred to the local settlement. Thus Headley (p. 77) signifies 'clearing overgrown by heather' and Hendon is 'the high hill'. But the modern suffix -*don* may be otherwise derived as in Essendon (p. 66) where it comes from OE *den*, a valley, signifying the valley of Eslas' people.

These instances will suffice to show that place-name study is both fascinating and complex. Unfortunately in inexpert hands it is a fertile field for idle guessing and speculation. It is essential to trace the derivation of the modern form of the name by comparing it with earlier variants as they appear, say, in the Domesday record, or in Saxon charters. Properly used, however, the study is an important auxiliary to geographical field-work since the names often reflect the former condition of the country or the factors controlling the first siting of the settlement. A few examples taken from the country here studied will illustrate this point and at the same time indicate some of the dangers of 'popular etymology'.

Esher (Aescaeron) is probably a compound of OE *aesc*, 'ash-tree', with one of the following: OE *sceran* to cut, *scearn*, boundary, or *scear*, ploughshare. It is suggested that the ridge on which it stands may have been likened to a ploughshare or that OE *scear* may have been used in the sense of 'border' or 'rim'. Leatherhead (Leodridan) includes the elements *leõde*, people and *rida*, riding path or ford. It can probably be interpreted as 'the public-ford'.

The first element of *Cobham* (Coveham) may be a personal name, or from OE *cofa*, 'a recess with precipitous sides in the steep flank of a hill', in the sense of cove. The great meander of the Mole with its river cliffs may well be the source of the name. *Brockham* (*Brocham*) is doubtful not only in the meaning of its -*ham* suffix, but in its other syllable which may be from either OE *brõc*, brook or marsh, or *brocc*, badger. It can thus be interpreted either as the 'farm or village by the stream or marsh', or as the 'badger meadow'. In the first case it would probably mark an early, in the second a later settlement (cf. p. 56).

The name *Mimms* (Mimmine) is of doubtful origin: it may embody a folk-name, *Mimmas*, and it is interesting to note that the surname Mimms still survives in the district. Alternatively, it has been sought to derive it from the late Latin word *mummus*, a mound. On this Mr F. Brittain, the historian of South Mimms, comments that there is in fact nothing to sustain the role of 'mound'. In such a case the geographer's 'eye for country' can perhaps supplement the historian's findings, for as a feature in the topography North Mimms Park rises as a distinct and unmistakable mound between North Mimms and South Mimms (p. 186).

If we now apply the evidence of *early* settlement to our region it is clear the features which for so long repelled prehistoric settlement had not ceased to operate, for pagan burial grounds are absent from the greater part of the area and early place-names are not numerous. Burial grounds are common in East Kent and coastal Sussex. A few are known in the valleys of the Thames and the Wandle and a few occur in the scarp-foot zone of the Chiltern Hills. South of the Thames the *-ingas* names are scarce (Tooting, Dorking, Tyting, near Guildford, Chevening) and over the greater part of the North London countryside west of the Lea they are completely absent, though Ealing and Yeading occur in south-west Middlesex. In Essex they are much commoner (Epping, Nazing, Havering, etc.). If we include names in *-ham* and *-ingham* our pattern of primary settlement is somewhat extended but the distribution is still thin. If we take wider ground the reason for this is plainly indicated. The first settlers were guided in their choice of sites by the availability of water and of the more readily cultivated loamy soils. Despite all the progress won during long centuries in the breaking-in of the heavy forest country it still offered hindrance to settlement. Throughout southern Britain as a whole the early place-names and burial grounds cluster persistently in areas of relatively light or readily arable soils and avoid the heavier country. But we are not primarily concerned here with the specialist task of the historical geographer in tracing the progress of settlement and any attempt to do so in detail may tend to obscure the fact that the greater part of our area was settled within a comparatively short space of time (say 500 years) and that the first great transformation of the landscape was thus effected. Very few of the settlements with which we are concerned are not named in the great Domesday record. This gives us an aggregate picture of the great episode of settlement as a whole and it is very instructive to compare the fully developed settlement pattern with the physical and geological features of the country.

The Evidence of Parish Boundaries

In the part of Surrey which we here study it is clear there are two major lines of villages situated respectively at the foot of the Chalk dip-slope where it adjoins the overlying Eocene beds, and at or near the foot of the Chalk escarpment in the 'Holmesdale zone'. The former, between Guildford and Croydon, include the following settlements: Merrow, West Clandon, East Clandon, West Horsley, East Horsley, Effingham, Little Bookham, Great Bookham, Fetcham, Leatherhead, Ashtead, Epsom, Ewell, Cuddington, Cheam, Sutton, Carshalton, Beddington. Including the terminal members there are thus twenty settlements ranged along a geological boundary over a distance of about 24 miles, at an average distance apart of about a mile. The second line of settlements includes Shalford, St Martha (Chilworth), Albury, Shere, Abinger, Wotton, Dorking, Betchworth, Buckland, Reigate, Gatton, Merstham, Godstone, Tandridge, Oxted and Limpsfield. In order to see the distribution of these settlements and their neighbours clearly we need to consider the parish boundaries which mark the original village territories (Fig. 17). The boundaries have been somewhat modified in later years with the creation of new parishes, and the elimination of outlying areas of one parish within the boundaries of a neighbour, but the essential pattern is clearly retained on the modern map. Both lines of settlement afford good examples of 'strip parishes', each parish with its major axis extending athwart the geological boundaries in a north–south direction. Thus the settlements of the northern line all include, more or less centrally, the narrow strip of the Lower London Tertiaries and extend thence northwards on to the London Clay and southwards over the Chalk dip-slope. Those of the southern line normally include a section of the scarp-crest and face and in most cases extend across the Lower Greensand outcrop to the Weald Clay. This extension is particularly striking in the country west of Dorking. Thus the parish of Abinger extends from a point about a mile north of the crest of the Chalk escarpment at Hackhurst Downs for 10 miles south to the county boundary. Its neighbour, Wotton, is of similar form. Shere, however, terminates southward on the Greensand dip-slope, adjoining the Weald Clay parish of Ewhurst which includes a small area of the high crest

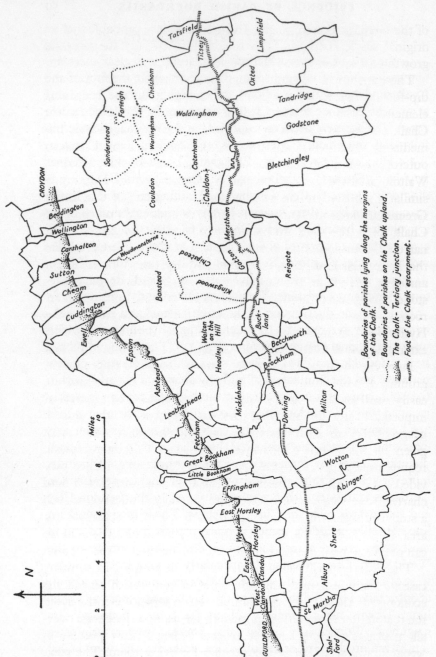

Fig. 17. Parish boundaries on the North Downs in Surrey

Tatsfield
Titsey
Limpsfield
Chelsham
Oxted
Farleigh
Woldingham
Tandridge
Sanderstead
Warlingham
Godstone
CROYDON
Caterham
Bletchingley
Beddington
Coulsdon
Chaldon
Wallington
Merstham
Carshalton
Woodmansterne
Gatton
Reigate
Sutton
Chipstead
Cheam
Banstead
Kingswood
Cuddington
Buck-
land
Ewell
Walton on the Hill
Betchworth
Epsom
Headley
Brockham
Ashtead
Mickleham
Milton
Leatherhead
Dorking
Fetcham
Great Bookham
Wotton
Little Bookham
Abinger
Effingham
East Horsley
Shere
West Horsley
Albury
East Clandon
St Martha
West Clandon
GUILDFORD
Shal-
ford

Miles

N

Boundaries of parishes lying along the margins
of the Chalk.
Boundaries of parishes on the Chalk upland.
The Chalk–Tertiary junction.
Foot of the Chalk escarpment.

of the Greensand escarpment. In such cases it is probable that an original single strip has been broken into two by the rise and growth of a settlement on the Weald Clay.

The parish map not only brings out the lines of scarp-foot and dip-foot settlements but renders it easy to fit in the remaining elements of the settlement pattern. West of the Mole where the Chalk outcrop is narrow the parishes of the two main lines immediately adjoin one another. East of the gap, with a much broader outcrop, room is left for a line of 'high plateau' parishes, Headley, Walton, Banstead, etc. The parish pattern east of Dorking is similarly adjusted to the varying form and width of the Lower Greensand outcrop. Betchworth parish extends from north of the Chalk scarp (the southern boundary of Headley Heath) across the narrow Greensand outcrop on to the Weald Clay, where it adjoins the large parish of Leigh lying wholly on that formation. Its analogue, Merstham parish, terminates southwards on the Folkestone Sands, since the widening of the Greensand outcrop leaves room for other villages on the summit of the low escarpment of the Hythe Beds, as at Nutfield and Bletchingley. Both these parishes extend far south over the Weald Clay.

Parish boundaries, although they can of course be traced on the ground, are not conspicuous features of the landscape and are easily overlooked in field study. Yet they cannot be ignored as important clues in studying the development of the human geography of an area. They illustrate the necessary supplement given by map-work to field-work and their full interpretation requires the support of place-name study and the evidence provided by old maps, including, in the final analysis, Saxon land charters where such are available. Into the full complication of such a study we cannot here enter; it has, in fact, hardly begun for our area. But it is clear that from the general pattern of settlement we can obtain some indication of the order or method of the process.

The orderly partitioning of the area so as to give, in so many cases, a share of contrasting land types in each parish reflects the economy of these early agricultural settlements. We must avoid the temptation to regard it, in modern terms, as a deliberate overall 'planning' of the land. It reflects rather a slow process of 'geographical selection', a competition for living room. The positive advantages offered by the two main settlement lines were of a clear and definite character. They gave access to relatively light readily ploughed soils. In the scarp-foot or Holmesdale zone these were provided by the Lower Chalk, the Upper Greensand and parts of the Lower Greensand, notably the Sandgate Beds. The heavy Gault Clay was everywhere avoided by settlement and was no doubt left in pasture and woodland. In the dip-foot zone readily arable soils were found on the narrow strip of the Lower London Tertiaries and on the lower part of the Chalk dip-slope, where the soil is enriched by the residue of the former Eocene cover. Both zones are favoured also in water supply. Springs occur on both margins of the Chalk outcrop and water can in any case be reached at a small depth in wells, both here and in many places on the Lower Greensand outcrop. Both zones therefore offer likely sites for *primary* settlement. There is abundant evidence indeed that, throughout the Weald, the margins were first settled, the interior wastes of woodland being drawn more slowly into the full economic system by the development of secondary settlement. The first villages were sited in the scarp-foot zone or on the Lower Greensand, with their arable fields and home pastures around them. But they also laid the Wealden woodlands under contribution, for timber, small wood for fuel, and as pasture grounds for their herds of pigs—'pannage for swine' as old documents often term it. Where the line of scarp-foot villages was single, the parish extended as a continuous tract into the Wealden woodlands. Where it was double, i.e. where a line of Lower Greensand villages grew up parallel with the scarp-foot series, the latter had no direct contact with the Wealden woodlands, but owned detached areas in the Weald which played the same economic role. In both cases the later sequence of events was generally the same; the outlying colonies of woodsmen and swineherds began to support themselves by cultivation in the forest clearings and these secondary settlements rose finally to full parish status, so that the original long strip of territory became subdivided (as probably in the case of Shere and Ewhurst); or the separate outlier of woodland pasture itself became a village unit. This process of subdivision, the development of secondary from primary settlement, is to some extent more clearly marked in Kent and Sussex than in Surrey, for there the Wealden settlements often carry the distinctive place-name suffix -*den* from OE *denn*, a swine pasture. But there is no reason to doubt that the evolution of the Surrey parishes took place on entirely similar lines. It is natural to enquire how far a similar form of economy and sequence of settlement applied to the second line of parishes in the 'dip-foot zone'. Little detailed attention has yet been given to this problem, but the country we shall study affords a few suggestive clues which can be supplemented from the map, and occasional documentary sources. Many of these parishes no doubt had tracts of woodland which could have been used as common pasturage on the London Clay; the survival of Commons at Effingham, Bookham, Ashtead and Epsom (pp. 72–5) is significant in this regard. But the extent of such areas was at best relatively small and in many cases it must have been cleared for cultivation at an early date. In any case the woodland must have been shared or subdivided along the common boundary with the parishes of the Wey, Mole and Thames valleys. Even though these resources were limited it is interesting and surprising to find evidence from pre-Conquest charters that Ewell, Cheam and Beddington had 'denes' in the Weald Clay area south of Tandridge, some 15 miles from the parent villages. It seems very probable moreover that the original dip-foot parishes east of the Mole extended into the higher Chalk country and thus embraced tracts of the Clay-with-flints woodland and perhaps heathland. This implies that the 'high plateau' parishes are of secondary origin, having served originally in some sense as 'wealds' for those of the dip-foot zone. For this supposition a certain amount of direct evidence exists. Thus the present parish of Kingswood separated by Banstead from the long strip parish of Ewell was in fact a detached part of the Ewell parish until late in the nineteenth century. Again, there is a possible clue in the place-name Walton. This is very common in 'lowland' England, but it was of several distinct derivations of which the chief are from OE *Wealatun—tūn* of the British, and OE *Wealdtun, tūn* in the Weald, i.e. in a wood. It is not always possible in an individual case to be sure which of these was the original form, but the situation of the place may evidently sometimes give a clue. Further, when the early derivative is *Waletone*, the former meaning is indicated, while *Waltone*, while not conclusive, generally indicates the latter. Surrey gives us examples of each, for Walton-on-Thames was *tūn* of the British, while Walton-on-the-Hill, with which we are now concerned, was *tūn* in the Weald. This incidentally reminds us that 'weald' as a place-name is not confined to the Weald of geologists and geographers, the Andreds weald of the Saxons; of this we shall find other evidence. But it further suggests that the wooded Chalk uplands may have afforded 'Wealds' for lowland parishes to the north. The general land pattern of the scarp-foot and dip-foot parishes was indeed closely similar. In both cases the parent settlement and its cultivated land lay centrally, but the parish passed into woodland or waste both at its northern or southern ends. The analogy can be clearly perceived if we compare, say, the parishes of Albury and Ashtead. In the former the 'terminal' wastes lay on the Chalk scarp-crest and the upper Hythe Beds dip-slope respectively. In the latter, prior to the separation of Headley parish, it lay northwards on the London Clay and southwards on the high Chalk plateau.

The North London country is, as we have seen, of much simpler geological constitution than the Weald; there is no such obvious zonation of land types and thus less opportunity, at first sight, of relating the village land units to the pattern of soil and vegetation. Nevertheless there is one feature in common between the two areas in the extensive 'background' of clayland forest. Though there is little evidence in the North London area of the earliest phase of Saxon settlement, we can still distinguish with some probability distinct primary and secondary settlements. The primary settlement favoured the area of lighter soil and readily accessible water on the river-drifts of the Thames, Lea and Colne valleys and the glacial drifts of the Vale of St Albans. These areas surround a 'core' of London Clay occupying the northern part of Middlesex and the adjacent entirely similar country of southern Hertfordshire. There is no doubt that this clayland was originally and indeed for long centuries following the settlement, heavily wooded and there are not wanting indications that it served in some sense as a 'weald' for the earlier marginal settlements and that, as in Surrey, secondary settlements ultimately became established within it. We note for example that the place-name 'weald' occurs in Harrow Weald (as also in the similar country of Western Essex —North Weald and South Weald). More significant still are the totals of woodland, recorded as 'pannage for swine' in the Domesday Book. We must remember that the date of this document is long after the beginning of the settlement; it may be taken as marking, roughly at least, the end of the settlement period. By this time an appreciable amount of the woodland had undoubtedly been cleared for cultivation and secondary settlements had been established within the woodlands and gained in many cases full independent status. Nevertheless the assessed totals of pannage for swine present the clearest evidence of substantial surviving woodland within or attached to some of the manorial territories of the time. The manors for which the assessed totals equal or exceed pannage for 1,000 swine are as follows: Hatfield, Cheshunt, Enfield, Edmonton, Hendon, Kingsbury, Harrow, Hillingdon, Harefield, Rickmansworth, Cassio (near Watford) and St Albans. For Hatfield, Edmonton, Cheshunt and Harrow the figure is as high as 2,000. These high forests records closely and almost completely encircle the London Clay country. The only other manor within the immediate area with a similar high total is Fulham (1,000), but this apparent exception does fall into line with the others, for the woodland of Fulham, earlier the property of the Abbey of St Albans, had passed before the time of Domesday into the possession of the Bishop of London's Fulham estate; the woodland in question was undoubtedly at or near Finchley.

The significance of these figures in locating the surviving forest of the time can be fully appreciated only in the light of the fact that many of the manors in both counties are credited with much smaller totals (generally less than 500) and that many of those within the riverine belt of the Thames have none. There can be no doubt therefore that large forest 'reserves' existed on the London Clay. Similar high totals are recorded for many of the Chiltern manors (e.g. Tring, Berkhamstead, Wendover, Risboro' and Bledlow), giving evidence of a wide forest cover on the high Chalk plateau, as in the case of the North Downs.

If we now study the parish boundaries (Fig. 18) in search of the type of clue we have found in the Weald we must of course avoid the assumption that the manner and arrangement of forest tenure and the sequence of resulting settlement was exactly the same in the two cases. Yet it is clear, at least, that many of the parishes, centred on the lighter and more readily cultivable lands of the marginal drifts, reached backwards into this forest hinterland in the fashion of strip-parishes. The parishes of Edmonton, Enfield,

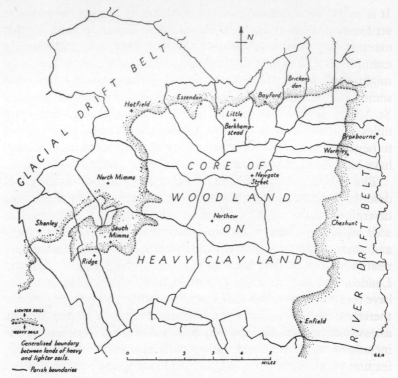

Fig. 18.   Parish boundaries in south-eastern Hertfordshire

Chesthunt, Wormley, etc. along the western side of the Lea valley
have this form. Enfield is a particularly clear case, for the wide
forest expanse of Enfield Chase, west of the parent settlement, was
not cleared for cultivation until late in the eighteenth century.
Strip parishes also occur along the northern edge of the clay
country adjoining the Vale of St Albans, as at Shenley, Ridge,
North Mimms, Essendon, Little Berkhamstead, Bayford, etc.
These, however, are of two types; in some cases, e.g. North Mimms,
Hatfield, the parent settlement lies in or on the margin of the Vale,
in others, e.g. Ridge, Essendon, the village lies on an 'island-site'
—a gravel-capped hill, within the clay country though its territory
extends into the lighter soil belt of the Vale. It is probable but not
easy to prove that the former type is the earlier of the two. Between
the northern and eastern lines of strip parishes room is left for
such a parish as Northaw lying wholly within the clay country.

It is probable that these arose by separation, around a secondary settlement, of the forest tract of one of the marginal villages. The exceptionally large and sprawling parish of Hatfield offers us an example in which such separation has not taken place though it might well have done so. The parish comprises a broad expanse of some 15 or more square miles in the drift country of the Vale of St Albans north of the village and a long 'pan-handle', some 5 miles in length, extending south-eastwards in the clay country to beyond Newgate Street, which as a plateau village might well have become the head of a separate parish.

The parish of South Mimms crossed by one of the routes described below (p. 179) lies like Northaw centrally between the diverging series of strip parishes. Here a local re-entrant of lighter soils within the clay country afforded attractive arable conditions and there is no reason to doubt that the settlement arose at a relatively early date. Much of the parish, however, lies on the London Clay and the original settlement and its arable land must have formed an island in the forest waste. It is interesting to notice therefore that South Mimms is not separately recognized and assessed in the Domesday record; it was for long attached to and included with the manor of Enfield, showing thus some of the features of a secondary settlement. Its area was in fact extended after the clearing of Enfield Chase, the land thus freed for cultivation being divided between South Mimms and Enfield.

6

Bibliography

There are few books devoted to the geography of south-east England, but there is a considerable literature, both books and papers, on particular aspects of the geography and on related subjects (geology, botany, agriculture, history, etc.). The following are works in which parts of our subject are more fully treated. References to literature on more local or more specialized subjects are given in the text, in footnotes, or at the ends of the sections.

1. DARBY, H. C.: *The Historical Geography of England before 1800.* Cambridge, 1948.
2. KENDRICK, T. D., and HAWKES, C. G.: *Recent Advances in the Archaeology of England and Wales.* Methuen.
3. MAWER, A., and STENTON, F. M.: *An Introduction to the Study of English Place Names.* English Place Name Society. Cambridge, 1933.
4. *Memoirs of the Geological Survey* (dealing with the geology of the country covered by the respective sheets of the one-inch Geological Map):

      239 (Hertford) 1924
      256 (North London) 1925
      257 (Romford) 1925
      270 (South London) 1921
      271 (Dartford) 1924
      285 (Aldershot) 1928
      286 (Reigate) 1932
      287 (Sevenoaks) (In preparation)

5. TANSLEY, A. G.: *Britain's Green Mantle.* Allen & Unwin, 1949.
6. TANSLEY, A. G.: *The British Islands and their Vegetation.* 2 vols. Cambridge, 1939.
7. TOPLEY, W.: *Geology of the Weald.* Memoirs of the Geological Survey, 1875.
8. WOOLDRIDGE, S. W.: 'The Glaciation of the London Basin'. *Quarterly Jour. Geol. Soc.* vol. 94 (1938), p. 627.
9. WOOLDRIDGE, S. W., and GOLDRING, F.: *The Weald.* New Naturalist Series, Collins, 1953.
10. WOOLDRIDGE, S. W., and HENDERSON, H. C. K.: *Some Aspects of the Physiography of the Eastern part of the London Basin.* Trans. Inst. Brit. Geographers, Publication No. 21. Geo. Philip, 1955.
11. WOOLDRIDGE, S. W., and LINTON, D. L.: *Structure Surface and Drainage in South-East England.* Geo. Philip, 1955.

III   The Juniper Hall Country

• •

1. Ashtead, Headley and Box Hill: the North Downs in Mid-Surrey

MAPS: One-inch Ordnance Survey New Popular, Sheet 170
   1 : 25,000 Ordnance Survey, Sheets TQ/15, TQ/16, TQ/25
   All but a very small area of the ground covered is included in
   Sheet 270 of the one-inch Geological Survey (Reigate)

WALKING DISTANCE: Route 1, 11 miles, subject to modification or
   division into separate excursions as suggested on p. 72

ACCESS: Train from Waterloo, or Green Line Coach, to Chessington;
   train from Waterloo, or Green Line Coach, to Ashtead. Return by
   train from Box Hill or by Green Line Coach from Burford Bridge
   or Mickleham. (See, however, the variants of the itinerary suggested
   below, p. 72)

This excursion is based on a N–S traverse of the North Downs,
beginning on the Eocene rocks at the margin of the London Basin,
ascending the dip-slope of the Chalk to the high plateau of the
Downs, and descending the scarp-face to the outer vale of the
Weald. The traverse or 'transect' method is the best way of
studying a scarp-land terrain such as we have on the outer flanks
of the Weald. By crossing the more or less parallel outcrops of the
rocks at right angles to the strike the observer becomes impressed
with the essential form and surface phenomena of each physiographic zone in the sequence. By repeating the process on a
number of selected lines of traverse he sees what are the constant
features of each zone, and what is the significance of local variation
in its form or land use. The reader is urged to make frequent
reference to the diagram, Fig. 20, which represents the geological
cross-section of the country along the line of traverse. Such cross-

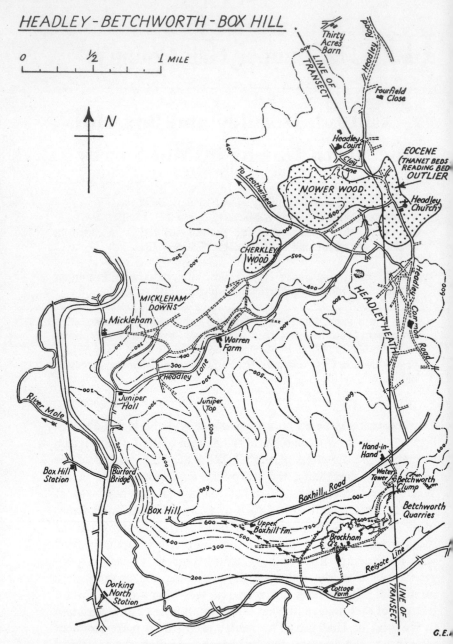

HEADLEY - BETCHWORTH - BOX HILL

0   ½   1 MILE

N

Thirty
Acres
Barn

Fourfield
Close

Headley
Court

EOCENE
(THANET BEDS
READING BED
OUTLIER

NOWER WOOD

Headley
Church

To Leatherhead

LINE OF TRANSECT

Clay
Lane

Headley Common Road

Headley Road

CHERKLEY
WOOD

HEADLEY HEATH

MICKLEHAM
DOWNS

Mickleham

Warren
Farm

Headley Lane

Juniper
Hall

Juniper
Top

River Mole

Hand-in-
Hand

Box Hill
Station

Burford
Bridge

Water
Tower

Betchworth
Clump

Betchworth
Quarries

Box Hill

Boxhill Road

Upper
Boxhill Fm.

Brockham Q

Dorking
North
Station

Cottage
Farm

Reigate Line

LINE OF TRANSECT

G.E.

Fig. 19

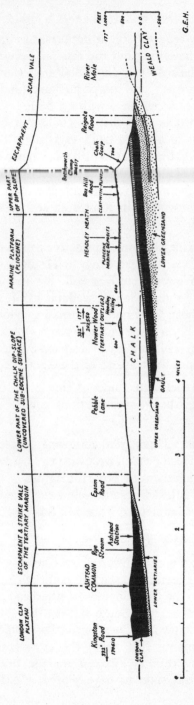

Fig. 20. Transect of the North Downs (Ashtead–Headley–Betchworth, Surrey)

The student will find it a useful exercise—draw this diagram to a larger scale and add notes on soil, vegetation, land-use, etc., of the ground traversed

sections, or transects, are every bit as important as the map of the particular area, for they bring out the relation between structure and surface which the map can only show imperfectly. Actually the map and the transect are complementary, and no graphic account of any region is complete without both.

The route described in this chapter could not be completed with all its variations in a single day's excursion. The following suggestions should help the reader to plan a journey within suitable limits of time and walking distance. The description is given of Route 1 as a whole, the minor variations being dealt with as they arise. The variations involved in Routes 4a and 4b are recorded separately at the end.

> *Route 1.* Begin at Chessington. Alternative routes over Ashtead Common, then via Ashtead Park to Headley and Headley Heath. Alternative routes to Box Hill.
> *Route 2.* Begin at Ashtead station, walking ½ mile north to join Route 1 on Ashtead Common. Continue as above.
> *Route 3.* Begin at Farm Lane on the Epsom–Ashtead road (bus and coach route). Follow Route 1 as from Ashtead Park, that is omitting most of the traverse of the Eocene country.

To make a more thorough study of this piece of the North Downs two separate whole-day excursions could be planned as follows:

> *Route 4a.* Begin at Chessington, following Route 1 as far as Headley. From Headley turn westward to Mickleham Downs. Return from Mickleham or Box Hill station.
> *Route 4b.* Begin at Mickleham and follow the Headley Valley to Headley Heath. Complete the round to Box Hill as in Route 1.

CHESSINGTON TO EPSOM COMMON (ROUTE 1)

The portion of the route southward from Chessington across the London Clay country assumes a starting point at Malden Rushett (172616), a hamlet on the Chessington–Leatherhead road. It is just over a mile from Chessington South station. The bus and coach stop at this point is known as Chessington Post Office.

Rushett Lane, running ESE from the cross-roads, traverses typical London Clay country. Except for the unenclosed and wooded common lands soon to be explored, the London Clay surface is a patchwork of fields, mostly small pastures, enclosed by wooded hedgerows with drainage ditches. There are numerous coppiced woods and strips of thicket, the woody growth everywhere dominated by oak.

There are various ways of entering the common land on the south side of Rushett Lane. The most direct route southward begins at Glanmire Farm (182612), but an interesting alternative is given below (p. 74). Follow the eastern side of the hedge which forms the boundary between Glanmire Farm and the wooded land of Epsom Common and keep on the high ground; any diversion to the left leads downhill to the broad valley floor occupied by the artificial lakes known as the Stew Ponds. Continue southward past an iron boundary post which marks the corner of Chessington, Epsom and Ashtead parishes. From this point the woodland path bends to a more south-easterly direction.

In this neighbourhood, at an altitude 200 to 225 feet O.D., the London Clay carries patches of flinty gravel. The woodland hereabouts inclines to the 'dry oakwood' type, oak being the dominant tree with a subsidiary growth of birch and hazel. There are occasional colonies of mature birch. The ground is almost completely covered by bracken and bramble. Over most of this stretch of wooded common land, however, the unrelieved clay soil supports the 'damp oakwood' plant communities with their more varied underwood and ground flora. That the clay soil remains wet and cold for a great part of the year is shown by the abundance of rushes (*Juncus* spp.) in the woods and rough grasslands of the area.

The footpath follows the boundary between Ashtead and Epsom parishes. On the Ordnance maps this line is shown as if dividing high forest on the one side (the part of Ashtead Common called The Forest) from open heathland (Epsom Common) on the other. The division is not so distinct as this because woody vegetation has in recent times invaded the margins of the common. Epsom Common is, however, fairly open ground—rough grassland rather than heath, with large areas in cultivation, the work of reclamation since the Second War.

South of the cottages in Newton Wood the footpath gradually descends into the broad valley of a stream called The Rye. It should be clear that we have here an example of drainage along a strike vale. The northern side of the vale, the slopes of Ashtead and Epsom Commons, is a degraded but nevertheless recognizable escarpment of the London Clay. The more gently sloping southern side is formed by the dip-slope of the Chalk and the lower divisions of the Eocene strata. The stream, by its lateral shifting down the dip-slope, has created a constantly receding escarpment near the southern margin of the Eocene mass. The transect (Fig. 20) shows the relation between surface features and strata in the neighbourhood of Ashtead. It may be noted that here the Rye is a typical 'subsequent' stream.

CHESSINGTON TO ASHTEAD COMMON (ROUTE 1A)

The form of the Eocene escarpment and the view southward over the Chalk dip-slope are better seen from the high ground immediately north of Ashtead station. It is possible to reach this more favourable view-point (181597) by taking a different route across Ashtead Common. This adds a little to the walking distance and may only find favour if a long day is contemplated, or if the route is to be completed in two separate excursions as suggested above.

Leaving Malden Rushett by way of Rushett Lane as already described, turn off to the right (176613) before reaching Glanmire Farm. The point is marked by a signpost at the roadside indicating a public footpath to Ashtead Common. The path first traverses a narrow strip of wooded land between grass fields and then enters The Forest at the point 178606. Within the woods the path maintains the SSE direction, passing near the site of a Roman villa at the summit of the hill. There is now nothing to be seen of the villa and associated remains except overgrown spoil heaps from the archaeologists' excavations. The footpath emerges from the woods on to open ground near the top of the clay escarpment at a point (181597) commanding a view over Ashtead towards the summit of the North Downs.

Between the view-point and Ashtead station the lower slopes of the escarpment are in cultivation. Cultivated land formerly extended on the other side of the Rye stream as far as the old village of Ashtead on the Epsom road. Now, however, a full square mile of this fertile land (lower Eocene sands and clay overlying Chalk) is occupied by suburban housing. Southward beyond Ashtead the rising ground of the Chalk dip-slope appears to be more thickly wooded than it actually is. The illusion is due to the low altitude of the view-point. The sky-line of this landscape is approximately the northern boundary of the high plateau of the Downs. On it may be seen the spire of Headley Church, and immediately to the right three low, wooded eminences standing a little above the otherwise uniform crest of the land. These lumps are the residual masses ('outliers') of Eocene material isolated far out on the Chalk dip slope. Still farther to the west the crest of the Downs is broken by the Mole gap. It is on the west side of the gap (Ranmore and Netley Heath) that the form of the Chalk dip-slope is best seen.

ASHTEAD STATION TO EPSOM COMMON (ROUTE 2)

If the excursion is begun at Ashtead station instead of Chessington the view from the slopes of Ashtead Common described above will be a useful introduction to the day's work. The vantage point is reached by way of the level crossing at the station, a short walk past the houses and the ascent of a track between cultivated fields to the edge of the woodland and scrub higher up the slope. Walkers arriving thus, and those who may have reached the same point by the alternative route from Rushett Lane, should now make their way eastward along the scarp-face to the point 187599 where the track along the boundary of Epsom Common crosses the Rye stream. Formerly the land south of this point was rough common and is still thus represented on the Ordnance maps. The footpaths across it, which are also shown on the maps, have not survived the post-war cultivation, so the short cut to the next level crossing (190595) cannot be made. The farm track running SSE to the crossing still exists, however, and to reach it the walker coming eastward along the London Clay escarpment should follow the foot track along the lower edge of the woodland and through the scrub on the right bank of the Rye stream until the substantial wooden bridge is reached. On his way he may notice how the cultivation of the clay land requires provision for the drainage of surface water. Heavy clay land can be made highly fertile, especially as here where drainage is made easier by the sloping surface.

EPSOM COMMON TO FARM LANE (ROUTES 1 AND 2)

The route towards the railway across the now cultivated part of Ashtead Common traverses the last surviving piece of open country between the built-up extensions of Ashtead and Epsom. Throughout historic time the country along the Chalk–Eocene junction has been a zone of closely spaced settlements linked together by roads (p. 59 and Fig. 17). Here, just beyond the fringe of Greater London, where the road along this line has become a major SW highway, paralleled with a suburban railway, the early villages and townships have expanded so much that they now form an almost continuous suburban belt.

Before crossing the railway (190595) the observer should look back at the line of the London Clay escarpment. In this prospect the form of the escarpment and its relation to the strike stream can be fully appreciated. South of the railway a broad track along the western margin of a wood leads to the Epsom Road beyond which the same alignment is maintained in Farm Lane, the next portion of the route.

FARM LANE TO HEADLEY (ROUTES I, 2 AND 3)

The London Clay surface, thinly covered in places by drift materials, continues southward as far as Park Farm. Beyond that point the Reading and the Thanet Beds outcrop in turn. In the gardens of the semi-rural villas along Farm Lane there is little to indicate these changes in the substratum. Even the passage on to Chalk a little south of Pleasure Pit Road is not at once evident. It is worth the short diversion to the left along Pleasure Pit Road to look at the old chalk quarry at the next road junction. The quarry is much overgrown and completely fenced in, but part of the face may be seen from the road. It discloses Chalk up to soil level with no overlying deposit.

It should be clear that Farm Lane runs along the unbroken surface of the dip-slope and that the valley parallel to it on the east side contains the north-flowing ('*consequent*') headstream of the Rye. Beyond Park Lane (198578) the rural landscape becomes more typical of Chalk country, though it is rather formalized by belts of trees (beech and conifers) along the borders of the culti-vated fields. At the cross-roads (200573) immediately south of Tudor Croft there comes into view an impressive forward pros-pect of the dissected dip-slope of the Chalk with Headley Church and the wooded eminences of the Eocene outliers along the sky-line. It is perhaps from this view-point better than any other that we realize the high gradient of the northern slopes of the Chalk. We are already 200 feet higher than the bed of the Rye stream at the foot of Epsom Common, and the high ground only a mile and a half ahead of us rises yet another 200 feet. The southerly route continues along the Headley Road which passes between extensive cultivated lands. Both to the east and west the ground falls away into broad valley bottoms. Across Langley Bottom on the east side may be seen the grandstand of the famous race-course high up on the slopes of Epsom Downs. Across the Ashtead valley westward the form of the dip-slope is perfectly displayed in the profile of the next interfluve.

At the fork in the road (202568) take the right-hand branch which drops a little down the side of the valley. Looking now in a NW direction down the valley it is possible to see back to the crest of the London Clay escarpment at Ashtead Common. Immediately about us on the side of the valley the character of the Chalk soil can be observed. On the cultivated land the soil contains abundant Chalk fragments and quantities of flint, derived directly from the underlying rock. The hedgerows and grass verges contain plants characteristic of the Chalk flora. A little farther south, however, in the banks of the sunken road beside Headley Park it will be seen that the Chalk surface is covered by varying thicknesses of loam containing occasional flint pebbles. This deposit on the slopes around the head of the valley can be accounted for in the light of what is presently to be seen.

Opposite the entrance to Headley Park (200556) it is worth while making a diversion to the right along the road signposted 'Leatherhead' in order to see a small chalk pit in Clay Lane, the next turning to the left. The pit is rather overgrown but the chalk face is accessible in places. The white Upper Chalk is seen grading into a surface soil derived wholly from the Chalk itself by weathering.

Continuing along Clay Lane towards Park Corner the observer will notice the sharp rise in the wooded ground behind the builder's yard (202551) and again at the road junction by the forge. This break of slope is seen to mark the base of the mass of Thanet Sand and Reading Beds resting on the Chalk. The Headley road lies in a deeply sunken trench in these Eocene strata, and although the road banks do not present a clean section of the beds, samples of the sands and loams at different levels can readily be obtained. The road between the forge and the Cock Hotel cuts across the eastern end of the Eocene outlier close to the smaller of its two flat summits at the 600-feet altitude. The whole mass is clothed with oakwoods (Nower Wood) which make a sharp break against the surrounding farm land. The Ordnance maps mark a *spring* at the base of the outlier, near the forge. A spring could hardly be expected where relatively impervious clays and loams form a summit *above* the permeable Chalk. The source of water at this and other points round the margin of the Eocene mass is surface drainage from the wooded slopes above, augmented at times by seepage from sandy layers in the Lower London Tertiaries. The eastern end of the Nower mass is known as Oyster Hill, from the occurrence of fossil oyster shells at one horizon in the Reading Beds.

At the point 204549 between Oyster Hill and the Cock Hotel walkers taking the Mickleham route (4a, p. 82) turn westward along the southern flank of Nower Hill, but those following Route 1 continue south. A variety of refreshment is obtainable at the Cock. It is worthwhile at this place to seek the view-point in the field just beyond the NE corner of the churchyard. Here the prospect is northward down the Chalk dip-slope towards Epsom, and to the middle Thames at Richmond and Kingston.

HEADLEY TO BETCHWORTH CLUMP

The road past the Cock runs southward along the plane of the Chalk plateau at an altitude of 570 to 600 feet O.D. The ground falls away to the east into the Walton–Epsom dry valley, and to the west into the head of the Headley valley. At the point 206542 the road turns SW to meet Headley Common Road and the open expanse of Headley Heath. The significance of this flat surface at the 600-feet altitude, with its cover of sand and coarse shingle, is discussed on pp. 17–18. Apart from its physiographic interest the great flat of Headley Heath is remarkable for the contrast of its natural vegetation with that of the neighbouring Chalk slopes. The dry sandy soil, poor in soluble minerals and acid in reaction, is agriculturally infertile. It supports only heather, bracken, gorse and the flowering plants and grasses characteristic of the dry heath community. The abundant growth of young birch which now occupies large areas may be the result of the decline of grazing concurrent with the increased popularity of the Heath as a public open space (p. 48).

From the northern end of the Heath excellent views of the Headley valley may be obtained. These should impress the observer with the great extent of the post-Pliocene denudation of the Chalk mass. The Eocene outliers of Cherkley Wood and Nower Wood (Fig. 19) are subdued, but still quite conspicuous, relief features on the northern rim of the valley. The view southward along the length of the level Heath shows in the distance the slightly rising ground beyond it towards the scarp-crest (Fig. 20). It is as if the observer were looking inland from the tidal flats of the Pliocene sea towards its low coast. The walk in that direction past the little cottage (204527) at the edge of the open part of the Heath does indeed cross the now indeterminate shore line of that ancient sea, bringing us on to the highest zone of the Chalk upland—the part which has remained a land surface since mid-Tertiary times. Along the straight track leading to the Box Hill road the inclination of the surface is readily noticed. It will be clear also that on this gentle slope there is clay soil—a marked change from the sand and shingle of the Heath. This derives from the layer of Clay-with-flints (p. 16) which here covers the Chalk. Excavations in this material for drainage on house sites by the Box Hill road revealed a thickness of 15 feet of bright red clay with abundant unworn flints. The woodland on the clay, as seen in Heath Plantation and Betchworth Hills Wood, is 'coppice-with-standards'. Woodland is interspersed with arable cultivation, giving the typical land-use pattern of the clay-covered areas of the North Downs plateau.

Turn right along the Box Hill road, and 300 yards on, opposite the 'Hand-in-Hand' (203520), enter the track leading to the Water Tower on the summit known as Betchworth Clump (732 feet O.D.). Here at the crest of the Chalk scarp a small piece of open ground above the rim of the Chalk quarries affords a convenient view-point for studying one of the most impressive prospects of the Weald. In the sector of the escarpment to the east, between Pebble Coombe and Colley Hill (Reigate), the Upper Greensand forms an almost level shelf or bench at the foot of the Chalk. It is distinguished also by its consistently cultivated surface and relatively few trees, as compared with the pasture land and woody growth on the lower-lying Gault belt adjacent to it. Immediately below the view-point, to the west of the quarries, the Upper Greensand outcrop is narrower—a single field in width. The Gault outcrop also is narrow, the Folkestone Beds of the Lower Greensand appearing in the sand pits on the south side of the Reigate Road. This compression of the outcrop belts is associated with the locally high dip of the beds, as the transect (Fig. 20) shows. South of the view-point the Lower Greensand outcrop does not stand in high relief, and is scarcely distinguishable from the lowland of the Weald Clay. To the east and west, however, the Greensand cuesta makes a bold feature in front of the Chalk range, although the two sectors are greatly different in height and width. With good visibility a number of well-known features in the more distant parts of the Weald can be seen from Betchworth Clump. These include Tilburstow Hill, a summit on the Greensand range to the east, Crowborough, ESE, the highest point in the High Weald, and a considerable length of the South Downs with Chanctonbury distinguished by its clump of trees. The South Downs come more into view as the crest of the intervening High Weald declines westward.

Most of the foreground of our view comprises the lowland developed on the Weald Clay. It is impressive to reflect that the reduction of the country to the level of this wide-spreading plain has been effected by normal river action since the uplift of the Pliocene sea floor, across which we were walking a few minutes since.

BETCHWORTH CLUMP TO BOX HILL

The least strenuous way of walking from Betchworth Clump to Box Hill is by the Box Hill road, an uninteresting and disagreeable mile and a half. The alternative is to go down the scarp-face by the track a little to the west of Betchworth quarries and ascend diagonally from the point 193508 north of Brockham (see map, Fig. 19). It may be added that this is a convenient point from which to reach the Reigate road for the bus service to Dorking, if it is desired to omit the climb to Box Hill. Readers who intend studying this part of the region fully may arrange to visit Box Hill on the occasion of the Mole Gap Excursion (see p. 85).

The scarp-face between Betchworth and Brockham quarries has a cover of chalk scrub in which it appears that Juniper is slowly yielding to the aggressive Yew, a form of succession which is commonly occurring on the downs, and may be connected with the change from a sheep-grazing régime to a completely wild condition (p. 48). At the foot of the steep slope the cultivated land on the Upper Greensand bench may be examined. If there are no standing crops the soil will be seen to contain fragments of the grey sandy limestone which constitutes this division. Below the disused lime works at Brockham there are pits (200509) in which the rock is exposed, but they are rather difficult of access on account of the dense scrub which now covers the old workings. In any exposed face the Upper Greensand looks quite like the Chalk, as it becomes white on weathering, but closer examination will show that the rock is much harder than chalk. It contains quartz grains and minute flakes of mica which sparkle in a freshly broken surface. It is worth while penetrating the overgrown pits below the Chalk, as the Gault clay is also exposed a little lower down.

The track along the scarp-foot is the so-called Pilgrims' Way which is referred to on p. 124. In this sector it follows characteristically the margin of the cultivated land and has the form of a terraced track along the hillside, lined in places with old yew trees. The ascent of the scarp from the point 193508 is first through a yew wood, then across the drive leading to Brockham Warren and on to the open slope below Upper Boxhill Farm (now a tea house). The high ground of this part of the Chalk scarp gives interesting views to the south and west, across Dorking and along the scarp vale. A great length of the Lower Greensand range can be seen, from Redlands Wood past Leith Hill to Coneyhurst and beyond. The Greensand plateau of Hindhead limits the view to the west. In that direction the most distant salient of the Chalk escarpment (White Downs) is on the line of the N–S watershed which crosses the scarp vale and divides the Mole and the Wey drainage systems. This watershed is seen to extend to the highest part of the Greensand dip-slope between the wind gaps at Coldharbour and Leith Hill.

The descent from Box Hill may be made either by the long spur running down into the Mole gap between Burford and Fredley, or by a steep track leading to the river at the foot of the

Box Hill cliff (p. 92). Either course will lead conveniently to the coach route or to Box Hill station.

HEADLEY TO MICKLEHAM (ROUTE 4a)

The lane branching westward from the point 204549 on the Headley road descends into the end of the Headley valley. At the next bend (200548) follow the contours of the valley, either along the track known as Langley Lane, or by way of the footpath almost parallel to it, to the Leatherhead–Reigate road. This part of the route coincides approximately with the southern edge of the Eocene outlier of Nower Wood. A speculative reconstruction of the land surface of early Pleistocene times could represent the embryo Headley valley as a subsequent valley along the foot of an Eocene escarpment, of which the outliers at Nower Wood and Cherkley Wood are the fragmented remains—a condition comparable with that of the present-day Ashtead Common scarp and the valley of the Rye stream below it.

At the Leatherhead–Reigate road (195545) the view down the Headley valley is of some interest. The spread of cultivation over the more gentle slopes near the valley head is in marked contrast with the narrow ribbon of farmed land lower down. The uniform plane of Headley Heath and the tops of the ridges between the tributary valleys to the west of it are well seen in this prospect.

Turn off the road at the point 193546 into the bridle road running SW towards Cherkley Wood. Just at the entrance of this track there is a view north-westward down the dip-slope and across the middle Thames. When visibility is good the Chilterns beyond Henley and Marlow can be seen.

The first 400 yards of the bridle road is on the Chalk surface at nearly 550 feet O.D. and the ground falls to the NW down the dissected dip-slope. Cherkeley Wood is seen to occupy a substantial mound above the Chalk surface. Its vegetation of oak and mixed underwood with bracken indicates a change to a non-calcareous soil. The wooded mound is a second and smaller Eocene outlier separated from the Nower Wood mass.

The bridle road leads into a long strip of open ground behind the crest of the scarped wall of the Headley valley. At the SW end of this open space there is a choice of routes. A footpath to Mickle-

ham Church and another to the north end of the village both
descend the eastern wall of the Mole gap—the degraded slope of
one of the pre-Glacial river cliffs (p. 90). Access to Mickleham
by either route is convenient for returning to London by coach.
Equally suitable for travellers by coach, but on a more direct line
to Box Hill station for those going by train, is the steep track down
the side of the Headley valley at the eastern end of Juniperhill
Wood. Before descending the track the view from the summit of
White Hill (179532) should be studied. This includes a southward prospect of the Leith Hill range seen through the entrance
to the Mole gap, and a view of the dry valleys cut deeply into the
high ground of Box Hill.

The Headley road in the bottom of the valley joins the Mickleham road near Juniper Hall, where there is a coach stop. Box Hill
station may be reached either by way of the Mickleham road and
Westhumble Lane, or better by entering the old drive of Fredley
(171525) and following the footpath over the main road, crossing
the river by the railway footbridge. Readers who have followed
the Mole valley excursions will recognize at Fredley a facet of the
200-foot terrace.

MICKLEHAM TO HEADLEY (ROUTE 4b)

This route is complementary to that of 4a, and deals with the
features of the Headley valley itself. The asymmetrical form of the
valley is well seen immediately E of Juniper Hall, where the steep
slope of Juniperhill Wood is opposed to the more gentle slope up
to Lodge Hill on the other side. Farther along the Headley road
(171525) the form of the Chalk surface is shown in the smooth
convexity of the higher slopes and the concave sweeps of the valley
bottoms, seen in both the main valley and the tributary Juniper
Bottom. An alternative to the road between this point and Warren
Farm is a footpath along the wooded slope of White Hill. The
vegetation of the slope consists of Chalk scrub, with an area of
maturing beechwood near the farm.

At Warren Farm, and elsewhere in the valley, there are relics
of an earlier floor (probably contemporary with the 200-foot floor
of the Mole valley) at a higher level than the present-day valley
bottom. These relics are not of any great size, but they are readily
recognized as flat surfaces on the spurs between the tributary

7

valleys (Fig. 21). The best examples are near Warren Farm (183531), the Lodge of Wentworth Hall (187535) and near the point 192536.

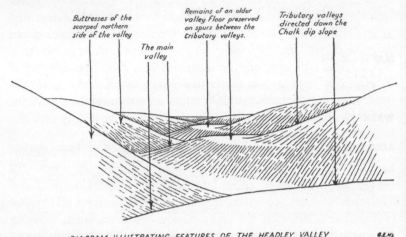

Buttresses of the scarped northern side of the valley

The main valley

Remains of an older valley floor preserved on spurs between the tributary valleys.

Tributary valleys directed down the Chalk dip slope

DIAGRAM ILLUSTRATING FEATURES OF THE HEADLEY VALLEY

Fig. 21

At Warren Farm there is a disused chalk pit exposing the lowest beds of the Upper Chalk. In the weathered section the joints and bedding planes of the rock are conspicuous, and lines of flint nodules occur. The disintegration of the Chalk near the soil surface can be well seen.

Immediately east of the farm another woodland path affords an alternative to the road for a short distance. It follows the lower contours of the bend in the valley, coming to the road again at 189536. From this point Headley Heath may be approached either by following the footpath round the site of Wentworth Hall (now demolished) and crossing the valleys near High Ashurst, or by continuing along the Headley road to the point 197540, where a footpath enters Dean Wood and ascends the valley side to the level surface of the Heath above. Various footpaths on the heath converge at 104527 with the track adopted in Route 1 (p. 72).

2. Leatherhead to Box Hill, Surrey: a Study of the Mole Gap

MAPS: One-inch Ordnance Survey, Sheet 170
    1 : 25,000 Ordnance Survey, Sheet TQ(51)/15
    One-inch Geological Survey, Sheet 286 (Reigate)

WALKING DISTANCE: 6½ miles

ACCESS: Train from London Bridge or Waterloo to Leatherhead, return from Box Hill (frequent services); or Green Line Coach, Service 712, 713 or 714, from London to Leatherhead, return from Burford Bridge on the same route.

The morphology and history of the river Mole are discussed on pp. 26–33. As so much of the history of Wealden denudation is recorded in the features of the river valleys which are cut through the Chalk an excursion devoted entirely to the study of one of these, the Mole gap, is fully justified. The study is primarily physical, and like that of the lower Mole (pp. 94–102) is much concerned with the identification of river terraces. But apart from its physical features as such, the Mole valley presents typical and very attractive Chalk scenery on account of the great amount of land bearing natural vegetation in the form of beechwoods and Chalk scrub. The wild downland of the valley sides makes a sharp break with the agricultural land on the gentle slopes and terraces towards the river. One of the most striking things about the valley bottom—more conspicuous indeed than the river itself which is largely concealed by trees—is its lines of communication, both road and railway, which link London with western Weald and the coast of West Sussex. The route through the Mole gap is one of the primary radials from London, though it should be added that it was relatively unimportant up to the beginning of the last century. Before that time there was little traffic into and across the western Weald, and even Dorking just south of the gap was a small and sequestered rural township. The Mole valley route opened up as a

85

branch of a much older highway—the one linking the settlements
of the Tertiary margin between Croydon and Guildford—which
had been for long one of the chief routes to the south-west of the
country. The gap road diverts from that line at Leatherhead, the
point at which the present study of the valley begins.

The ground covered in this itinerary is shown centrally within
the sheet lines of all the relevant published maps. Sheet 170 of the
one-inch Ordnance map shows almost the whole of the Mole
basin. Sheet TQ 15 of the 1 : 25,000 series gives the perfect repre-
sentation of the Mole gap and the high ground of the Chalk on
both sides. Cross-sections of the river valley should be sketched
in the field from the features actually observed, such as terraces,
river cliffs and other forms of slope (see Fig. 22). The one-inch

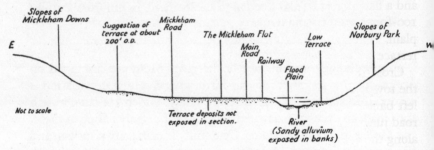

Fig. 22. Section across the Mole valley at Mickleham showing the
terrace sequence

Geological Map has certain limitations as a guide to morphological
study because, according to the convention of geologists, river
terraces are mapped (or ignored) on the evidence afforded by the
existence of a reasonable thickness of gravel or other alluvial
deposits. The presence of deposits is not the only criterion by
which a former flood-plain is to be admitted, although most terraces do represent the plains of deposition corresponding with the
successive gradings of the river. Again, an apparently continuous
gravel spread may represent more than one stage in the lowering
of a valley floor, but unless the stages are marked by striking
changes in level the geologist may not concern himself with
their differentiation. The published geological map gives only
a generalized picture of the conditions of the Mole valley
floor.

THE MOLE AT LEATHERHEAD

Travellers by train to Leatherhead, leaving the station by the exit on the down side, should cross the Cobham road (A245) and follow the footpath between the railway and the recreation ground; then, at the end of the footpath, turn right and pass under the railway bridges. Bus or Green Line Coach passengers alighting in Leatherhead may reach this point by walking from North Street, past the New Bull Hotel and along Station Road. Beyond the railway bridges the road runs between small factories and workshops and leads to Randalls Park and the riverside meadows (Common Meadow) on the west side of the town.

At the west end of the factory and sports ground of the Ronson Company there is clearly a level flood-plain bordering the river and a flat-topped terrace some 25 feet above it. It happens that the 100-foot contour just here coincides with the margin of the flood-plain. The latter is separated from the higher ground of the terrace by a distinct bluff.

Cross the meadow to the river bank and walk upstream along the towpath, passing under two railway bridges. Cross over to the left bank by way of one of the two road bridges and go on to the road junction at 161562. From here turn into the track which runs along the E side of Leatherhead Cricket Ground and continues as a footpath towards Thorncroft. The surface here is a terrace only a few feet above that of the flood-plain. In the sequence of levels present in the Chalk gap we may designate this the *Low Terrace*.* It is a fairly constant feature of the valley floor between Leatherhead and Box Hill.

THORNCROFT (LEATHERHEAD) TO MICKLEHAM BRIDGE

The footpath continues on the low terrace across the lane from Thorncroft Bridge. In the fields above, a small facet of the higher terrace (125 feet O.D.) breaks the gentle slope of the valley side. It will be observed that the valley near Leatherhead is very wide

---

* The reader may wish to correlate the terrace stages here with those observed on the Cobham excursion. The flood-plain at Leatherhead corresponds with the flood-plain at Stoke d'Abernon—the surface which farther downstream becomes the Cobham terrace (equivalent to the Taplow terrace of the Thames); the Randalls Park terrace at Leatherhead is the equivalent of the surface at Cobham Park, Plain's Hill and Fairmile Common—the Boyn Hill stage of the Thames (see also Fig. 12).

and shallow, for here at the dip-foot of the Chalk the ground is generally at low altitude. To the south the Chalk valley sides are seen to increase in height and steepness. Between the end of the fenced land at Thorncroft and the bridge of the Leatherhead By-pass the footpath runs near the edge of the low terrace; the drop to flood-plain level is here clearly discernible. Near the bridge (164553) the terrace and the footpath come close to the river bank.

The road bridge has lately been reconstructed, and the works included the cutting off of a small meander upstream; the old channel was filled in with the material excavated for the straight cut. This material consisted of sandy silt, which is the substance of the Mole alluvium throughout the length of the gap. South of these river works the low terrace disappears for a space, the side of the valley being a regular slope down to the flood-plain. A little farther south (164546) the flood-plain itself is eliminated from this left bank and a river cliff is cut in the valley side. On the opposite bank a narrow belt of flood-plain rests at the foot of a gently graded 'slip-off slope'. The cliff is continued towards Icehouse Combe, but along its southward extension the alluvial flood-plain is built against its foot.

We now come to one of the major meanders of the valley—not in this case a meander of the stream within its flood plain, but a deeply incised bend in the Chalk trench itself. The Norbury feature is a good example of an *ingrown meander*, that is one in which downcutting has been accompanied by lateral shifting of the river course. The main features are clear—a long spur of chalk running out eastward from the high ground of Norbury at over 400 feet altitude, flattening to form a broad toe just above river level at the Priory; this is opposed by the long concave sweep of the steep slope on the Mickleham side of the valley. The down-stream migration of the meander is best shown by the contrast between the steepness of the southern flank of the Norbury spur and the more gentle slope of its north-easterly side, which comes into view as we enter Norbury Park near Icehouse Combe.

The footpath to the Priory, and the farm road beyond, are on the low ground round the foot of the Norbury spur. It will be seen that this ground consists of a crescent of flood-plain bordered by an inner crescent of low terrace—the surface on which the Priory and other buildings stand. These features are very well seen in the northward view from Mickleham Bridge.

MICKLEHAM BRIDGE TO SWANWORTH FARM

From Mickleham Bridge the view southward reveals in part the great complementary meander of the valley extending to Burford. This bend is of compound form and its details may be studied on the journey upstream. It begins at Mickleham Bridge with a curved line of river cliff on the left bank forming the steep southern flank of the Norbury spur. A footpath runs along this slope high above the river. The ground is occupied by tall trees, mostly beech, so that views into the valleys are rather restricted.

At the Mickleham end the cliff is degraded, as the river is not there eroding its base, but immediately south of the railway viaduct (164537) there has been recent erosion, and the slope as a whole stands at a high angle. Here the foot of the cliff may be reached by going to the end of the steep part of the slope and returning on a footpath close to the edge of the river. When the level of water in the river is low it is possible to see here the action of the swallow holes—openings in the Chalk through which river water passes down to subterranean channels. It should be noted that between Box Hill and Thorncroft (Leatherhead) the water-table in the Chalk is some distance below the bottom of the river bed and that leakage from the river into the underground reservoirs and channels is always taking place. Leakage is restricted, however, because the spaces in the Chalk are relatively small and tortuous, and easily choked with debris; also the bed of alluvium which the river has laid down tends to seal the surface of the Chalk and check loss from the river channel. Where the river impinges on solid Chalk, as at the foot of a meander cliff, erosion exposes fresh joints and fissures in the rock, and at such places the water leaks away more freely. Normally river water enters the Mole gap in sufficient quantities to maintain a continuous surface stream as well as feed the underground drainage, but in a dry summer the diminished flow is entirely taken by the swallows at Box Hill, Ham Bank, Cowslip Bank, the railway viaduct and elsewhere. Then the river bed from the viaduct down to Thorncroft becomes streamless, and is occupied only by a chain of stagnant pools. At

Thorncroft the water-table comes to the level of the river bed so that here springs break into it and the surface flow is restored.

To see the passage of water into the swallow holes the level of the river must be such that the edge of the stream just comes to the foot of the vertical faces at the bottom of the meander cliffs. Then, by clearing away floating and submerged debris, and dislodging a few loose blocks of chalk, a spectacular flow of water down the fissures can be established. In places it is possible to push a flexible stick many feet down into the Chalk and clear the way for a copious flow of water. Unlike the harder limestones the Chalk does not form underground solution cavities of great size. Solution takes place just as rapidly in the Chalk, but as water passages increase in size they invariably collapse, causing surface subsidence. This has occurred frequently along the floor and sides of the Mole valley.

The path along the river bank to Swanworth Farm is private, but there is an advantage in going by an alternative track to the point 161535 on the high slope of Norbury Park in that it gives an excellent general view of the southern half of the gap. The high slope also is of some interest. Its concave sweep is a continuation of the slope we have traversed from Mickleham Bridge, and it goes on towards Westhumble, making an almost perfect semi-circle. Its highest parts—Beechy Wood, Druids Grove and the slopes immediately below Norbury—are the degraded remains of earlier river cliffs of the Mole valley (p. 33 and Fig. 13). Opposed to the concave line of the Norbury cliffs is the buttress of Juniper Hill and Fredley jutting out into the valley and cloven by the trench of the Headley valley. This feature is not seen to full advantage from any view-point on the Norbury side because of the tall trees which everywhere intervene. The present river no longer passes round the Norbury–Mickleham bend in a single meander. After passing Ham Bank it swings over to the right, where it cuts off the end of the Fredley spur (Cowslip Bank), returning to form the semi-circle of the Swanworth meander. About this set of three meanders there are disposed the segments of various terraces which may now be examined. The reader may commence this study by referring to Fig. 22 which shows a cross-section of the valley through Swanworth Farm and eastward along Swanworth Lane to Mickleham.

SWANWORTH FARM TO BOX HILL STATION

In order to appreciate the clear-cut terrace sequence it is necessary to make a diversion from the route along the valley side and to
traverse a portion of the cross-section. Descend, therefore, from
the point 161535 by the track along the field boundary to Swanworth Bridge. Here the difference in level between the flood-plain
and the low terrace on the left bank of the river is clearly seen.
The flood-plain on the right bank lies at the foot of a higher terrace
which will be readily identified with the Randalls Park (Leatherhead) stage. Cross the bridge and pass through Swanworth Farm,
ascending the bluff of this feature. To see the extent of the terrace
surface (the 'Mickleham Flat') pass over the railway level crossing
and the main road into Swanworth Lane, observing from there
the site of Mickleham village at the inner edge of the terrace and
the slopes of Mickleham Downs beyond.

It is best to return from Swanworth Lane by the same route to
the point 162535 and follow the footpath along the wooded slopes
to Ham Bank. This ground presents excellent examples of the
natural vegetation of the Chalk, including beech-yew woodland
and several variants of the scrub community containing a wealth
of species representative of the Chalk flora. The belt of natural
vegetation on these higher slopes ends abruptly against the cultivated land and pasture of the terraces of the valley bottom.

Between the margin of Beechy Wood and the top of Ham Bank
is a narrow remnant of the old valley floor at the 200-foot level
partly buried beneath material derived from the wasting of the
Chalk slopes above. Ham Bank is the uninterrupted drop from this
level down to the river, a cliff some 70 feet in height. Its features
are best observed from the left bank of the river near the sharp
bend in its course (161526). It is interesting to observe the difference in slope between the length of the cliff with which the river is
still in contact and the part of it to the south-east where flood-
plain alluvium has been built against its foot, protecting it from
recent river erosion.

From Ham Bank to the railway a footpath runs close to the
river bank. Follow this, first through the wooded ground (Nicol's
Field), and then along the meadows. From any point here (164524)
the terraced arrangement of the lower parts of the valley may again

be noticed. The river is bordered on both banks by a strip of flood-plain. That on the right bank is cultivated land, an exception to the general practice of keeping the flood lands in permanent pasture. Cultivation is continued across the surface of the low terrace. Beyond the house (165528: Cowslip Cottage) which stands at the inner edge of the terrace is the sharply rising flank of the Fredley spur, with its flat summit at the 200-foot level—another remnant of the higher valley floor. The spur is artificially cut in two places to carry the railway and the main road through it, both approximately at the level of the Mickleham flat (140 feet O.D.). On the left bank of the Mole silt has been piled on the inner margin of the flood-plain so as to leave the low terrace standing only three or four feet higher in level, but the feature is well preserved. The flood-plain is trenched with a U-shaped meander, now dry, but cut off artificially to expedite the drainage of flood water. The banks of the old river channel here reveal the sandy alluvium of the flood-plain. Farther back from the river the ground again rises to a 200-foot flat at Westhumble. At the end of the meadow (166523) a footpath beside the railway embankment leads to West-humble (Box Hill station). From here it is only a short distance to a point (165519) where the 200-foot surface may be observed.

BOX HILL STATION TO THE BOX HILL RIVER CLIFF

The last, and highly interesting, feature of the Mole gap to be included in this itinerary is the great river cliff which forms the western flank of Box Hill. This may be reached by various routes, of which perhaps the most instructive is that through Burford Meadows on the flood-plain of the river. From Box Hill station walk eastward along Westhumble Lane, cross the main road, and enter the meadows near the subway. At this point an impressive view of the cliff is seen; it is a surface inclined at about 45 degrees, nearly 400 feet in vertical height and aligned on the shallow con-cave curve of a major meander. The irregularity of the surface of the flood-plain at Burford is due to subsidence. The higher ground at the level of the main road is another portion of the Mickleham stage terrace.

The erosion phenomena of the Box Hill cliff are best studied from the footpath which runs along its length. To reach this, go to the southern end of the meadows, preferably following the river bank, crossing the river at the stepping stones (172513). From here the cliff path returns in the downstream direction, following roughly the contours of the slope 50 to 100 feet above the river. It will be seen that the Chalk surface is everywhere disintegrated by the agencies of weathering, and by the penetration of tree roots. The fragments and small particles of chalk descend the slope in large quantities, aided by rainwash during periods of heavy or sudden precipitation; there is marked gullying in places. The material is ultimately removed from the foot of the slope when the river is in spate. When erosion at the foot of the cliff is most active and the scree is transported as fast as it arrives at the bottom, falls of solid chalk may occur. These result in the creation of vertical facets at the base of the cliff. Large falls are frequently caused also by the uprooting of trees on the slope. It will be observed that trees on this surface have a precarious existence. Where the slope is steepest the tall-growing trees such as beech and ash fail to maintain roothold, and the ground is occupied exclusively by the tenacious box and yew. The establishment of plant competitors is restricted not only by the instability of the surface, but by the dense shade cast by the evergreen foliage of the box and yew trees themselves. Their own seedlings are tolerant of the rigorous conditions, and although few of the trees survive to great age and size, the community is readily regenerated. There is every reason to suppose that the box-yew cover has existed on this slope from remote times.*

The cliff path ends on the open ground of the long spur of Box Hill just above the Burford Bridge Hotel. It may be convenient to end the study at this point for the return to London by road or rail, but if time permits the ascent of the spur by the well-worn track will reward the observer with a view of the Mole gap as a whole, and with the resources of the Fort Tea Gardens, available at all seasons of the year.

* The natural vegetation of this and neighbouring areas is described in *The Book of Box Hill*, by G. E. Hutchings, obtainable from The Warden, Juniper Hall Field Centre, Dorking, price 2s. 4d. post free.

3. Great Bookham, Cobham and Oxshott, Surrey: River Terraces of the Lower Mole

MAPS: One-inch Ordnance Survey, Sheet 170
    1 : 25,000 Ordnance Survey, Sheets TQ(51)/05, 06, 15, 16 (only a
    very small part of the itinerary falls in the area of Sheets 05 and
    06)
    One-inch Geological Survey, Sheets 269, 270, 285, 286 (only a small
    part of the itinerary falls in the area of sheets 269 and 285)

WALKING DISTANCE: 11 miles (the route as described may be divided in
two by using railway access to Cobham)

ACCESS: Train from London Bridge or Waterloo to Bookham, return
from Oxshott (frequent services)

This excursion is in country wholly within the belt of the Tertiary (Eocene) rocks which lie between the Thames and the North Downs Chalk. It affords a study of the low plateau of the London Clay and of the sequence of river terraces which are so well preserved across the broad floor of the Mole valley in this lower end of its basin. An interesting feature of this sector of the Mole is the 'knick-point' at Downside Mill near Cobham where the river drops to a new level. Downstream from this point a new flood-plain appears at the lower level, the old flood-plain standing as a terrace above it (Figs. 11, 12 and 24).

The excursion route is conveniently placed near the centre of the area of Sheet 170 of the one-inch Ordnance map, but on the larger scale maps and the geological sheets it crosses and re-crosses the sheet boundaries. Very little of the detail, however, comes on the western sheets of either series, so that if the reader is not provided with these the sketch map (Fig. 23) will supply the essentials for guidance on the parts of the route not shown on the principal sheets.

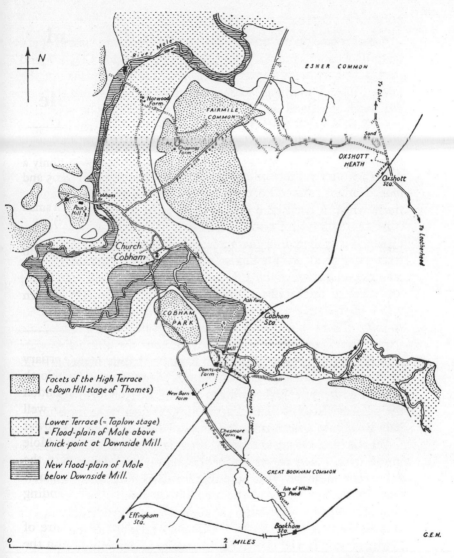

Fig. 23. Map of the flood-plain and terraces of the Mole near
Cobham, Surrey

BOOKHAM STATION TO DOWNSIDE MILL

A wicket gate on the up-side platform of Bookham station opens on to Bookham Common, a wild tract of the London Clay lowland stretching northward for a mile towards the broad valley of the lower Mole. A footpath follows a shallow stream valley through the rough grassland and scrub of the Common. The stream is crossed by a small brick bridge (124561), the footpath joining a cinder track near a small settlement called Isle of White. After crossing the outlet of Isle of White Pond the route is continued in a north-westerly direction along the main track through the Common. Natural oakwood occupies rising ground to the right of the track, which is itself on a belt of more open scrub land.

At 121567 a bridge crosses the north-flowing Chesmore stream in which is gathered all the surface drainage of the London Clay tract comprised in Bookham and Effingham Commons. The maturing planation of the London Clay surface is well seen in the low relief of this drainage unit. Chesmore Farm in the shallow valley of the stream presents a typical picture of London Clay country. There is no footpath along the valley of the Chesmore stream to its confluence with the Mole, but the alternative walk towards Downside along Bookham Road on slightly higher ground to the west is instructive, as it affords views southward beyond Bookham where the high, uniform crest of the North Downs forms the sky-line. At New Barn Farm (114577) turn right from Bookham Road into a farm track leading to Downside Farm (117581).

On reaching Downside Farm, turn right beside the farmhouse into a track which passes under the railway and descends to the flood-plain meadows. It is here that the Chesmore stream emerges from its shallow valley in the London Clay and flows on to the Mole flood-plain. The latter is a surface of considerable extent at a uniform level of 80 feet O.D.; its relation to the slightly higher ground is well shown in the profile of the railway embankment which carries the line from an adjacent surface at 100 feet O.D. across the plain at that level. Leave the farm track just E of the railway bridge and cross to the NE corner of the meadow to the bank of the Mole to see the fine prospect of the great flood-plain towards Stoke d'Abernon. The river flows along the southern margin of the plain against the foot of a river cliff about 70 feet in total height. Being cut in the unstable London Clay the surface of this cliff has been degraded by slipping; it is overgrown with scrub and woodland (Muggeridge Wood). The flood-plain itself is almost wholly meadow land; a copse of alder and ash occupies an area encircled by the meander of the river E of the railway line.

Returning to Downside Farm, leave the farm premises by the N entrance, and just beside the modern house turn right to see Downside Mill. The land around the mill is not easily accessible, and the crossing of the river here is on private ground. It is not easy, therefore, to observe the natural features of the Mole at this point, but it is clear enough that the river falls suddenly to a lower level. The mill was established here by reason of this natural circumstance; it had not required the construction of a dam and mill pond, which is the usual procedure when a mill is set up on a part of a river which has a uniform low gradient.

THE ENVIRONS OF COBHAM

The drop in the level of the river at Downside Mill becomes evident if we study the ground a little farther downstream. Go northward from the corner of the lane (116583), following a footpath through the meadows to Ash Ford (120590). Here we see ground at three different levels (Fig. 24). That on the left bank of the river on which we stand is the flood-plain. On the opposite bank an extensive terrace, some 10 feet higher in level, borders the flood-plain; its edge forms a distinct bluff, but at the site of the disused ford the sharp bend of a meander cuts into the terrace exposing in a small cliff layers of gravel and loam resting on London Clay. The approach to the ford on that bank of the river is in a small stream gully cut through the terrace. When the level of the river is low, water can be seen seeping from the base of the terrace gravel. The third surface level to be seen from Ash Ford is that of the summit of Cobham Park away to the left. It rests at about 60 feet above the flood-plain (125 feet O.D.) and is a facet of a higher terrace of the river of which other portions will be seen elsewhere down the valley.

We may now establish a correlation of two of these level surfaces. The low terrace, or Cobham terrace as we may now call it, has its surface a little below the height of 80 feet O.D., which is the same as that of the Stoke d'Abernon flood-plain observed

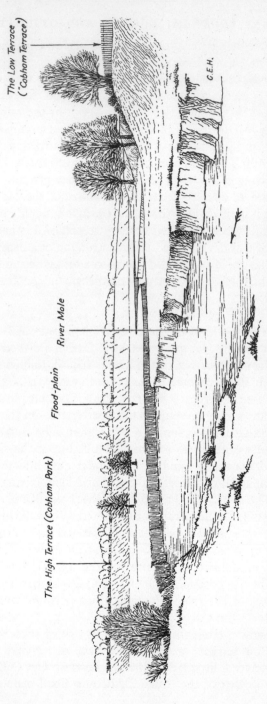

The Low Terrace ("Cobham Terrace.")

River Mole

Flood-plain

The High Terrace (Cobham Park)

G.E.H.

Fig. 24. Sketch of the Mole at Ash Ford, Cobham, showing the flood-plain and terraces

upstream of Downside Mill. The Cobham flood-plain is about
10 feet below this level, so it should be clear that in the vicinity
of Downside Mill we have the conditions illustrated diagrammatically in Figs. 11 and 12, namely a cut-back bringing the
valley floor to a lower level, with the 'knick-point' situated at
Downside Mill.

The crossing of the Mole at Ash Ford cannot now be made in
the ordinary condition of the river, even in summer. To get to
Cobham it is therefore necessary to return to the neighbourhood
of Downside Mill (116583) and follow the lane round the south
and west sides of Cobham Park. The rise to the level of the high
terrace should be noted, together with indications of the sandy
Claygate Beds resting on the London Clay on this high ground.
The geological map (Sheet 270) shows in addition a small patch of
Bagshot Beds capped by gravel on the level summit of Cobham
Park (125 feet O.D.), but this ground is not accessible.

To the south and west of Cobham the Mole executes a striking
series of meanders. The major sweeps are incised in the higher
ground, on which considerable tracts of the older terraces are
preserved, while the minor bends represent the lateral swing of the
river course within the bounds of the present-day flood-plain. To
follow the river downstream from Church Cobham would entail
many miles of walking. In order to see the terraces below Cobham
we must therefore cut across the great meander to the south-west.
We do so by keeping on the slightly raised ground (the Cobham
terrace) on which the parts of the village (Church Cobham and
Street Cobham) are built.

From the W side of Cobham Park the road descends to the
flood-plain near Downside Bridge (107595). After crossing the
bridge, turn NE towards the Church. A diversion to the east will
enable the reader to link up the site of Cobham with ground
already studied upstream at Ash Ford. Pass through the churchyard into Church Street and at its eastern end turn right to descend
River Hill, significantly named in that here the road drops from
the level of the terrace to the margin of the river. The map shows
clearly the conditions at this end of the village: a well-rounded
meander loop of the river encloses a large alluvial flat; on the
Cobham side of the bend (the concave bank) the river has cut into
the terrace, as at Ash Ford. The cliff feature here has evidently

8

been destroyed by the creation of a road alongside the river, but it will be seen that the nearby houses are built up on the terrace surface, while their front gardens occupy the slope down to river and road level. At the point 111599 another ford crossed the Mole; the track over the flood-plain on the far side of the river can be clearly discerned.

Return to Church Street, and at Pyports (107598) turn NNW into the straight footpath through cultivated fields on the surface of the Cobham terrace. At the corner of the Portsmouth Road continue WNW to Cobham Bridge (099605). Here the river Mole assumes a northerly course after its wanderings round the great meander. Seen from the bridge the valley downstream exhibits the same elements of morphology as we have seen at Ash Ford—the alluvial flood-plain, here much narrower, a bluff rising abruptly on the left to the plane of the high terrace at Pains Hill and Burwood, and a lower but still quite conspicuous bluff along the eastern margin of the flood-plain rising to the surface of the Cobham terrace. In this part of the river course the flood-plain stands at about 50 feet O.D., the Cobham terrace at 70 feet or a little below, and the high terrace at just over 100 feet O.D. The flood-plain (about 68 feet at Church Cobham) is thus seen to incline rather more rapidly downstream than do either of the two terraces by which it is flanked.

COBHAM TO FAIRMILE COMMON VIA NORWOOD FARM

From Cobham Bridge return along the Portsmouth Road, turn ENE, still on the main road, to a point 107606, and there turn N into Old Common Road, a track which runs for more than a mile on the almost level surface of the Cobham terrace. In passing along this road it becomes clear that the flat is bordered on the west by ground at a consistently higher level. North of the Common the Cobham terrace is seen to be extensively cultivated around Norwood Farm. The part of the road towards the farm is private, but is open for public access to Burhill Bridge by courtesy of the Burhill Estates Company. The open ground beyond Norwood Farm shows the great expanse of the Cobham terrace in this neighbourhood, as well as its perfectly graded surface. The light sandy soil with flint fragments and pebbles which can be seen on the cultivated land indicates the substratum of alluvial gravel.

Along the road eastward from Norwood Farm the bluff of the higher terrace is reached within 500 yards. Ascend the wooded slope by the track which now turns southward, passing a house called West Lodge. Just beyond this point the track comes on to open ground on a remarkably flat surface at 100 feet O.D., an extensive facet of the higher terrace. The southward view extends to the far-off crest of the North Downs. About a mile away to the SE may be seen the conspicuous white house, Pain's Hill, which stands on another piece of the 100-foot terrace just beyond Cobham Bridge. In the approach to Chippings Farm there are disused gravel workings (111615) where the composition of the higher terrace deposits may be examined. They are seen to consist of an assortment of flint stones—large water-rolled nodules, angular and worn fragments and pebbles—and fragments of stone from the Lower Greensand, all in a sandy matrix. These materials are clearly products of Wealden denudation, in part brought here at the time of the destruction of the rocks, but also derived from the dispersal of still older river deposits which lay at higher levels in Mole basin.

Between the gravel pits and West Lodge enter the wood eastward through a gate and follow a footpath towards the open heath on Fairmile Common. The small wood shows vegetation characteristic of dry gravel soil, oak, pine and birch forming the tree canopy, with abundant bracken and gorse in the field layer. East of the wood a broad belt of open heath extends to the main road. Much of the ground is bare and the leached sandy soil with its abundant flint pebbles from the gravel of the terrace can be easily examined.

FAIRMILE COMMON TO OXSHOTT

Cross the Portsmouth road at the point (123620) where it begins the descent into Spa Bottom, and enter the woodland track which remains for some distance on the terrace surface, but rises south-eastward to the higher ground of the sandy Bagshot Beds. The latter material forms the greater part of Esher Common and Oxshott Heath. The woodland here is of the same type as on the sandy gravel of Fairmile, and which is seen wherever the soil is basically siliceous sand, whether on Lower Greensand rocks, Eocene beds or gravel spreads. On reaching Sandy Lane turn E towards Oxshott Heath, passing numerous villas typical of Surrey's suburban settlement which, in units of varying size, has come to occupy areas of the dry heathlands over all the north-western part of the country.

Just beyond a house called Woodside Cottage, where the road bends to the left, strike up through the pine wood along a track marked 'Horse Ride'. As the track approaches the summit of the hill, a plateau at the 200-foot O.D. level, divert to the left to examine the Bagshot Beds capped by flint gravel which are exposed in a large disused pit. The face of the section has been largely covered by the accumulation of fallen material, but the yellow sand of the Bagshots is visible everywhere. It should be noted that the gravel capping contains besides pebbles and fragments of flint a proportion of sandstone and chert from the Lower Greensand, a common constituent of gravels of the 200-foot plateau in the London Basin.

A track running southward away from the pit leads to the edge of the Oxshott plateau where there is an impressive view of the lower part of the Mole basin and of the dip-slope of the Chalk. In this south-westerly prospect of the narrowing Chalk outcrop the range has all the appearance of a great wall along the margin of the Weald. The Weald itself is of course not visible from here, but the defile of the Mole gap is clearly cut in the sky-line of the view. Being viewed obliquely the gap appears singularly narrow.

Oxshott station, where our route ends, is at the foot of the scarped edge of the plateau.

4. Dorking and Leith Hill—the Greensand Hills and the Western Weald

MAPS: One-inch Ordnance Survey, Sheet 170
    1 : 25,000 Ordnance Survey, Sheet TQ(51)/14
    One-inch Geological Survey, Sheet 286 (Reigate)

WALKING DISTANCE: 9 miles

ACCESS: Train from London Bridge or Waterloo to Dorking North, returning from Holmwood on the same line, or Green Line Coach to Dorking

The object of the excursion is to traverse the dissected dip-slope of the Lower Greensand rocks from the lower parts of the Gault vale between Dorking and Westcott to the high crest line of the Leith Hill escarpment overlooking the western end of the inner Weald. From a number of vantage points on the Greensand hill country the features of the North Downs are to be seen in N and NE prospect.

Reference to the transect (Fig. 26) will show that the stony Hythe Beds which appear to form the body of the Leith Hill range are in reality only a capping some 200–250 feet thick above the mass of the underlying Weald Clay. Some of the streams on the dip-slope have already cut through the Hythe Beds into the clay, a fact which is revealed by variation in the vegetation and land use in the valleys. Between Leith Hill and Coldharbour the process of recession of the Greensand escarpment by landslipping as a result of spring and seepage action may be observed.

The views from the tower on Leith Hill (the highest summit in south-eastern England) give perhaps the best general picture of the western Weald and its relation to the encircling Chalk upland. Moreover, the elevation here is such that there can be an unobstructed view across the crest of the North Downs into the

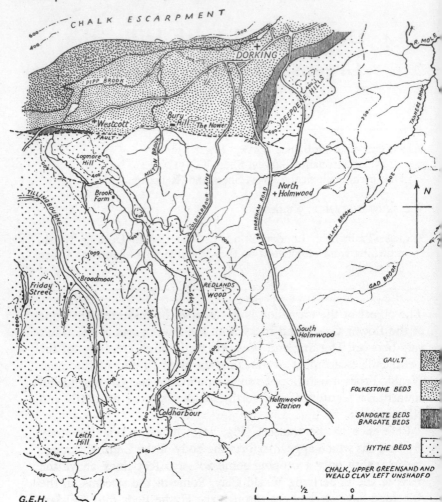

Fig. 25.   Geological map of the country between Dorking and Leith Hill,
Surrey (after H. A. Hayward)

London Basin and to the dip-slope of the Chilterns beyond. To
the south a great part of the range of the South Downs comes into
view and affords some points of contrast in form with the opposing
Chalk range on the northern side of the Weald.

The whole of the ground covered by this route is represented
on sheet TQ(51)/14 of the 1 : 25,000 map and also falls centrally
in the area of sheet 170 of the one-inch map. Sheet 51/14 shows all

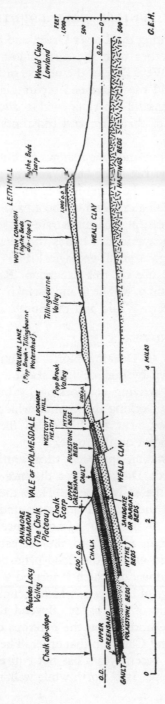

Fig. 26. Section of the North Downs and the Greensand upland (Ranmore–Leith Hill, Surrey)

the streams representing the Lower Greensand contribution to the Mole drainage, together with the easternmost tributaries of the neighbouring river Wey. One of the objects of the excursion is to recognize in the field the watershed separating the two drainage systems on the Greensand dip-slope, and to discern the manner in which land masses of this form and constitution are reduced by erosion.

Sheet 170 of the one-inch map shows all but the southern and eastern extremities of the Mole basin, and the greater part of this area may be seen from the summit of Leith Hill.

The one-inch Geological Map of the area (Sheet 286, Reigate) should not be used except to demonstrate the *general* rock pattern of the region. In inexperienced hands the details represented on it can be misleading. A small geological map (Fig. 25) has been specially drawn for use on this excursion. Bartholomew's half-inch map, sheets 6 and 9, will be found useful in identifying distant features of the western Weald and the South Downs.

DORKING TO THE NOWER

Train passengers to Dorking North station may pass to the west side of the town by bus, or walk about 1 mile partly in the town itself. Those arriving at Dorking by bus or Green Line Coach may go on to Dorking Bus Station which is on the western outskirts of the town near the hill called the Nower, the first important vantage point on the route.

From Dorking station-approach turn south and follow the London road towards Dorking for a distance of 200 yards to a point just beyond the railway arch. Here the Pipp Brook, the western tributary of the river Mole, passes under the road and is here within ½ mile of the point of confluence. A footpath runs alongside the old mill pond into the recreation ground. This ground has been laid out on the flood-plain of the stream. The string of water meadows of which it formed a part was formerly the natural boundary of the town, which occupied only the slopes on the southern side of the valley. Beyond the flood-plain the rising ground to the north is on the outcrops of the Gault Clay, Upper Greensand and Chalk, in that order. The northward expansion of the town in recent years has not entirely closed over the open land of this slope. It is worth while walking up the footpath

out of the recreation ground as far as the railway in order to see
the changes of soil type as the narrow outcrops are crossed.

Returning to the recreation ground and crossing the brook, enter
Mill Lane and the alley going uphill to the churchyard. In this
older part of Dorking notice the variety of local building materials
used. Pass through the churchyard into Church Street, which
leads to the Guildford road at Star Corner. About 100 yards
farther west turn left into Vincents Lane. Along the W side of this
road is a series of large sand pits (some of them now occupied
by small industrial works) in which the Folkestone Beds of the
Lower Greensand Series are well exposed. It is this formation of
compact brown and gold-coloured sand on which the town of
Dorking is built.

At the junction of Vincents Lane and South Street (near the
bus station) continue uphill in the southward direction along Coldharbour Lane from which there are entrances to the public open
space known as the Nower. Entering, say, by the small gate well
up the hill opposite Harrow Road West, ascend the footpath to a
point (161484) near the summit of the Nower ridge.

VIEWS FROM THE NOWER

The northward prospect from this point affords one of the best
views of the Mole gap. The general form of the valley is that of a
very wide, flat-bottomed trench with steep sides. The most striking feature of the gap is the western face of Box Hill, a steep cliff
over 300 feet high.

The valley bottom is cut off from view by a long, low spur of
Chalk which runs out across the entrance of the gap from the
foot of Denbies Hill on the western side. On the crest of the
spur is a facet of the old valley floor at the 200-foot level (see
pp. 32–3).

From this view-point on the Nower no great length of the
south-facing scarp of the Chalk can be seen. The southern face of
Box Hill, however, presents typical features, including the abrupt
change of land use between the cultivation of the lower slopes and
the wild scrub and sward of the steeper slopes above. On the scarp-
face of Denbies Hill the same zones are present, but the wild downland is here replaced by more formal parkland. The narrow ribbon
of the Gault outcrop along the lowest ground between the Chalk

and the rising surface of the Lower Greensand is obscured from view by houses and trees.

Turning attention now to the Lower Greensand country itself, the observer should take up a new position farther west on the Nower ridge in order to obtain a view to the south and south-west. At the foot of the south-facing slope of the Nower the Folkestone Beds are faulted against the Weald Clay, which here forms the floor of a broad hollow in the Greensand upland. The unbroken dip-slope of the Hythe Beds is seen in the crest of the Tillingbourne–Pipp Brook watershed. This ridge declines regularly from an altitude of over 900 feet near Coldharbour to 400 feet where it merges with the floor of the Gault vale. Eastward of this ridge the Hythe Beds dip-slope is poorly preserved. Its dissection has been effected by three drainage networks—those of the Pipp Brook, Milton Brook and Tanners Brook—separated by the low watersheds marked by Logmore Lane and Coldharbour Lane respectively, which branch out from the northern end of the high land of Redlands Wood. The three catchment areas can be readily traced on the map (O.S. Sheet TQ 14, or Fig. 25) and identified in the landscape. The broad hollow S of the Nower ridge is in part the basin of the Milton Brook but includes also to the E the low ground drained by the headstreams of Tanners Brook. The three watersheds are seen to be successively lower in altitude from west to east signifying the eastward wasting of the Greensand hill mass.

THE PIPP BROOK BASIN

The first part of the route over the Greensand country is generally in a SW direction across the valleys and watersheds to Friday Street, but this cannot be followed as a straight line from the Nower. It is necessary first to go westward along the ridge and traverse its northern slope to the foot of Bury Hill, following the drive which enters the former parkland from Milton Heath. Before turning south round the end of Bury Hill it is worth while pausing on the high ground near the cottage (150485) to note the passage of the Milton Brook through its gap in the ridge of the Folkestone Beds.

A track occupying a deep trench in the sandy Folkestone Beds passes round the western end of Bury Hill and joins the lane beside the Milton Brook. The lane continues into the grounds of

Bury Hill house, but a bridle path strikes off to the right through an iron gate (150483) and follows the Milton Brook upstream in a direction due south. On the left is the high retaining embankment of the Bury Hill lake, an artificial landscape feature.

Follow the bridle path for a distance of 80 yards from the gate, then turn right to cross the brook by a foot bridge and enter a stretch of park land on the Weald Clay. A fairly well-defined public footpath traverses this land in a south-westerly direction. Evidence of the clay substratum may be seen in the drainage ditches along the margins of the fields. Towards the summit of the Logmore ridge light sandy soil proclaims the remnant of Greensand cover on this higher ground. From the fields adjacent to Logmore Lane it is possible to look back over the Milton Brook catchment to the slopes of the Nower ridge, and beyond this to the Chalk scarp.

Readers using the 1 : 25,000 map may have observed a point of interest concerning the Logmore watershed. At the end of Logmore Lane (148468) a col on the watershed marks the abandoned course of the Milton Brook before its headwaters were captured by the neighbouring Pipp Brook. The latter stream exhibits a right-angled elbow of capture immediately below the col. The truncated Milton Brook is a good example of a *misfit* or *underfit* stream, out of keeping with the large size of the Bury Hill basin. A diversion from the direct route in order to see these features is well worth while; if it is adopted the crest of the next watershed (Tillingbourne–Pipp Brook) can be reached by way of Squires Farm. Otherwise the route from Logmore Lane continues south-westward across the Pipp Brook at Brook Farm, past the former Isolation Hospital and Logmore Farm, to the crest of the high watershed at the point 138465.

This excellent view-point is threatened by the upgrowth of a belt of coniferous woodland planted on the hillside in 1952, but it will serve geographical observers for a few more years, giving them one of the most instructive and beautiful prospects of the northern margins of the Weald.

THE TILLINGBOURNE

The footpath from Logmore Farm crosses Wolvens Lane, a bridle road running along the crest of the watershed, and goes down the side of the Tillingbourne valley along the edge of Stable Copse. At the bottom of the slope follow the Tillingbourne valley road for 100 yards southward and cross the stream in the meadows by a well-marked causeway (134464). At this point well down its course the Tillingbourne flows at a reduced gradient, and has established a flood-plain. This is easily recognized as the strip of flat ground along the valley floor. The stream just here has been modified by the erection of dams for a series of fish ponds. At a height of 15 feet or so above the flood-plain there are relics of an older valley floor which stands out in places as a fairly well-defined terrace. On the W side of the valley the footpath ascends the wooded slope, turning first to the right and then to the left, and leads to Sheephouse Lane, a road running along the next watershed. It is possible to reach Leith Hill by a route in a direct line with Sheephouse Lane, but an alternative which affords places of refreshment is the track along the next valley passing through the hamlet of Friday Street. This may be reached by the footpath crossing Sheephouse Lane at the point 132457.

VEGETATION OF THE LEITH HILL COUNTRY

In the country around Friday Street, as indeed over the whole of the southern part of the Hythe Beds country, there is an almost continuous cover of natural and semi-natural vegetation characteristic of the siliceous soils derived from this rock. The only breaks in the natural vegetation are the few small and widely scattered farms and a number of forest plantations. The rest is a vast waste of heath and neglected woodland, much prized according to present-day taste for its rugged beauty, but almost wholly unproductive. The higher and more arid situations are frequently dominated by heather, ling or bilberry, though the Scots Pine grows freely on the high ground and occasionally forms closed communities. Much of the bracken which dominates hill-top and valley alike may have suppressed heather in quite recent times. Bracken is generally condemned for its monotonous appearance, its exclusion of all smaller plants, and the difficulty of its eradication from land required for agriculture or forestry. But bracken, unlike heather, is a rapid and efficient soil improver and a safeguard against erosion. It is therefore an asset in terms of land potential and will no doubt be so valued when it becomes necessary to exploit all the soil resources of the country. Birch is almost everywhere present on the Hythe Beds soils. Beech grows well on most slopes and oak flourishes in the moist valley bottoms and particularly on the Weald Clay. Large quantities of prime oak have in recent years been harvested from the Pipp Brook valley, but that part of the area had for long been more carefully tended than the surrounding higher ground. The stony soils of this hill country, though poor and difficult to cultivate, are capable of profitable production. A good example of their capacity is to be seen at Anstiebury, NE of Coldharbour.

FRIDAY STREET TO LEITH HILL

The footpath S of Friday Street follows the stream along Abinger Bottom and joins the Abinger road at the point 127439. Follow this road southward to just beyond the drive of Highashes, and enter the quarry in the side of Highashes Hill (129436; the quarry is not marked on the map). Here the Hythe Beds are well exposed, showing sandstone interstratified with sand and beds of hard chert. The soil also is seen in section, but a better example of the leached or *'podsolized'* soil formed from the Hythe Beds is shown in a smaller pit on the same side of the road 200 yards farther south. From this place, and from Starveall Corner (131432) footpaths lead up the western flank of Leith Hill, over ground, clothed with heath, bracken and patches of pinewood.

THE VIEWS FROM LEITH HILL

The summit of Leith Hill lies at 965 feet O.D., and is surmounted by a tower 64 feet high, built by an eighteenth-century landowner in order, as his inscribed statement tells us, that the traveller may see the beautiful earth in all directions. Our own apathetic generation does little justice to the memory of this geographical benefactor in that it allows pine trees to obstruct part of the northward prospect. When visibility is at its best a vast area of south-eastern England comes into view from the top of the tower. It extends from the Oxfordshire Chilterns to the Channel, and from the Chalk uplands of Hampshire to the Weald of mid-Kent and East Sussex; the broad floor of the Thames basin between Windsor and Central London can at such times be clearly seen.

We may begin the study of this varied and extensive view by considering the two principal elements in its morphology. The first is a series of connected lowlands in relatively subdued relief; they comprise a great part of the Weald and the central belt of the London basin—the plains of the present-day river basins. The second element consists of the remnants of an older uplifted plain preserved only in the widely scattered summits and plateaux of the highest hills. The lower-lying surface is the product of a long process of land sculpture during which all but these few areas of the ancient high-level plain have been destroyed. The surviving fragments, such as Leith Hill and neighbouring summits (800 to over 900 feet), Blackdown (918 feet), Hindhead (890 feet), the highest parts of the North Downs, the South Downs and the Chilterns (700 to nearly 900 feet) and the centre of the High Weald (Crowborough Beacon, 792 feet), crown the hills which stand in long ranges above the general lowland level of the region. At places on the flanks of these ranges, chiefly on the Chalk, and on a few summits scattered over the lowland, there are facets of sub-sidiary younger plains which mark particular stages of down-cutting. Of these we have elsewhere noted the Pliocene littoral at 600 feet and the late Pliocene or early Pleistocene surface at 400 feet, as well as the terrace stages of the river basins.

Taking the points of the compass in turn we see in the northern prospect not only much of the ground covered by this excursion, from the Mole gap to the crest of the Greensand hills, but a number of more distant features familiar to those who have followed other of the excursion routes. On the North Downs various points on the scarp-crest will be recognized—Ranmore, Box Hill, Betchworth Clump, Colley Hill (Reigate) and the distant salient between Godstone and Oxted. The Eocene outliers at Headley can be readily distinguished, and in line with them (roughly NNE) is Central London. Slightly W of N the reservoirs near Staines mark the Thames gravel plain in Middlesex. It is in that direction and still farther towards the west that the distant crest of the central Chilterns may sometimes be seen.

Immediately east of the tower, almost at its foot, the Greensand scarp is cut back into the head of the Tillingbourne valley, making a deep col in the crest-line. Across it the high ground of Cold-harbour Common cuts off the view of the near parts of the Low

Weald, but far to the east the upstanding masses of the Chalk (Oxted), the Greensand (Crockham Hill) and the High Weald (Crowborough) present a profile which is typical of the familiar N–S transect of the great anticline.

At the foot of the tower on the south side the ground falls away almost precipitously to the level of the Coldharbour road. This is the true scarp-face of the Hythe Beds, and below it the surface of the Weald Clay descends more gradually to the general level of the plain. The difference in the character of the vegetation above and below the line of the road is quite striking. In the middle distance of the view the low-lying surface of the Weald Clay is seen extending southward past the end of the diminished mass of the High Weald. Beyond it the irregular crest of the South Downs intercepts the natural horizon, except along a line a little E of S, where the sea is occasionally visible through the river gap of the Adur. The still larger gaps of the Ouse, far to the east, and the Arun to the west are not conspicuous in the view from Leith Hill, as they are on oblique lines. It is of interest to note that most of the Low Weald lying to the S and SW of Leith Hill is drained by the Arun, whose headstreams have captured territory which formerly belonged to the catchments of the Wey and the Mole (Fig. 14), to the extent that they now receive drainage from the southern slopes of the Leith Hill range.

The southern outcrop of the Lower Greensand does not present a conspicuous hill feature except to the west of the Arun, where it is seen to rise in altitude and to stand farther forward of the line of the South Downs. Towards the extreme western end of the Weald its bold escarpment is closely opposed to that of the northern outcrop marked by the great bastion of Blackdown (Fig. 9).

The westerly prospect from Leith Hill Tower is dominated by the high land of the Greensand country which appears as a series of plateaux of increasing breadth, their scarped edges standing successively farther south towards the central axis of the Weald. The profiles of these successive sectors of the upland show clearly the break of slope between the true scarp of the Hythe Beds and the broad glacis of the underlying Weald Clay. The Hampshire Chalk is visible to the south of Blackdown and also through the Haslemere depression in the Blackdown–Hindhead plateau.

LEITH HILL TO COLDHARBOUR—THE HYTHE BEDS SCARP

East of the tower a track goes down into the col between the head of the Tillingbourne valley and the top of Cockshot Hollow. The latter is a small obsequent coombe in the scarp-face, with a sharply incised rain gully down it. Descend the gully to Cockshot Farm and turn eastward along the Coldharbour road, which marks roughly the line of the base of the Hythe Beds. From the road the observer will notice the difference in slope between the scarp of the Hythe Beds above and the surface of the Weald Clay below. It will also become evident that the whole of this hillside is a zone of instability. Its irregularity is the result of landslips, large and small, and of various ages. At the point 146432 one of the most recently disturbed areas may be examined. The wooded ground above the road is here seen to consist of a series of terraces, each representing a thick slice of the Hythe Beds which has descended and slid forward over the yielding mass of Weald Clay which had failed to support it. Farther along the road, between Coldharbour Church and the School, where the scarp-face is less wooded, the whole surface is terraced as a result of this type of movement. Below the road the irregularity of the Weald Clay slope is partly due to surface waves or folds in the clay itself, but partly also to the existence of disintegrated masses of Hythe Beds resting upon it, the relics of older landslides. Some of these relict masses lie far out on the lower parts of the slope.

It would appear that the large hollow or combe between Coldharbour and Anstiebury marks the breaking up of a substantial rectangular mass of the Hythe Beds which formed the SE corner of the plateau. The removal of this mass has exposed the head of the Pipp Brook valley in the col between Anstiebury and Coldharbour Common. The siting of Coldharbour at this point is of some interest.

The best view down the Pipp Brook valley is from the road junction (154442), ¼ mile ENE of the village. Before entering the track (50 yards along the Holmwood branch of the road) to Anstiebury Farm the site of the Iron Age earthwork known as Anstiebury Camp may be inspected. Its southern and western flanks are part of the natural scarp-face, but on the east and north the site is encircled by a double wall and ditch of imposing dimensions.

Similar earthworks on Holmbury Hill and at Hascombe are of known Iron Age date, suggesting permanent settlement on the Greensand upland at that period (p. 53).

The magnificent eastward prospect from the open ground above Anstiebury Farm includes the portion of the Low Weald S of Brockham and Betchworth which is cut off from the view from Leith Hill tower. Over this stretch of the Weald Clay between Holmwood and Park Hill, Reigate, the river Mole and its tributaries occupy what is in effect an exaggerated river gap in the Greensand range.

The cultivated land on the eastern slope of Anstiebury provides indisputable evidence of the fertility of the Hythe Beds soil, at least on certain horizons. The ground here is stony and dries all too readily, but it regularly yields satisfactory crops. At the farm a footpath strikes ESE from the track and descends to a point (163437) on Moorhurst Road. The lower parts of the slope exhibit the irregularity of surface and variation in soil which is characteristic of the process of scarp formation by landslipping, the younger stages of which we have noted at Leith Hill and Coldharbour.

Holmwood station and the bus route to Dorking are within ¾ mile walk along Moorhurst Road.

5. West Clandon, Albury and Guildford: a Study of the North Downs and the Holmesdale East of the Wey Gap

MAPS: One-inch Ordnance Survey, Sheet 170
  1 : 25,000 Ordnance Survey, Sheets TQ(51)/04 and 05
  One-inch Geological Survey, Sheet 285 (Aldershot)

WALKING DISTANCE (including diversion): 10 miles

ACCESS: Train from Waterloo, via Leatherhead to West Clandon. Return from Guildford by same line or Main Line

This route illustrates interesting and important variants of the features seen around Dorking. The high dip of the Chalk reduces its outcrop to a width of only $1\frac{1}{2}$ miles and the rocks south of the escarpment are similarly affected by the great monoclinal fold, of which the Hog's Back, west of Guildford, marks the northern limb. Immediately to the south runs the line of the Peasemarsh fold, the most northerly of the Wealden anticlines. The Tillingbourne, a subsequent tributary of the Wey, has developed its valley along the anticlinal axis, so that at Albury it flows between inward-facing escarpments of the Bargate Beds and Folkestone Sands. The former, inconspicuous near Dorking, here expand considerably and affect both soils and landforms in important respects. These several factors combine to put a new impress on the detail of the country, which is in notable contrast with that of eastern Surrey.

THE TERTIARY MARGIN AND THE CHALK DIP-FOOT

On leaving the station approach at Clandon turn left and follow the road southwards to Clandon cross-roads. Near our starting point the upper surface of the Chalk, beneath the Tertiary cover, lies at a depth of about 300 feet. For nearly a mile the route crosses London Clay, but between the school and the church the Reading Beds emerge at the surface. These make little surface sign, combining with the London Clay to give a country dominantly of pasture and woodland. This is best studied from the train between Effingham and Clandon, for the buildings of the village of West Clandon, strung along the north–south road, afford us only scanty glimpses of the country through which we are passing. Beyond the church we cross on to the Chalk and at Clandon cross-roads the dip-slope of the Downs rises steeply ahead. Here the sudden change of the landscape on the margin of the Eocene outcrop can be well seen. The main east–west road runs on the Chalk through a strip of dominantly arable country on the lower dip-slope. Here must have lain the early arable lands of the dip-foot settlements. As late as 1794, before the great parliamentary enclosures, there were 300 acres of unenclosed arable land in East and West Clandon and 450 at Bookham. Springs break out near the Tertiary junction, as, for example, by the ponds in Clandon Park, west of the church. Where wells penetrate the Tertiary cover to the Chalk the water has risen in some cases above ground level. At the pumping station of the Woking waterworks, south of the cross-roads, the boring is wholly in Chalk, the water-level being 90 feet from the surface, at about 225 feet O.D.

Take the footpath signposted to Newlands Corner which starts a few yards west of the cross-roads. This passes through a plantation of conifers and then, as the ground rises, through beech plantations, but the characteristic Chalk shrubs, notably dogwood, are conspicuous along the path which reveals a light sandy soil with many flints: the sand is probably a residue of the former Reading Beds cover. Beyond the plantation the path enters mixed woodland with hazel undergrowth and emerges on more open ground covered with Chalk scrub. Here watch for a cross-path

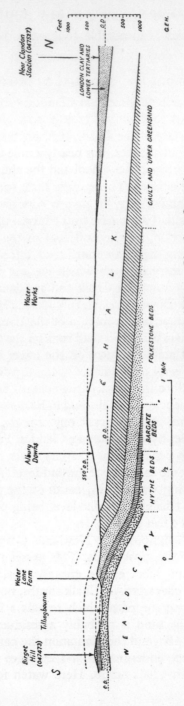

Fig. 27. Section of the North Downs (Albury–Clandon, Surrey)

which returns (left) to the road just south of an old chalk pit. In this pit a well-marked flint band near the top of the face indicates a northerly dip of about 4–5° and a good section is given of the thin black soil characteristically developed on Chalk slopes throughout the area.

THE CHALK PLATEAU

From the road, or better from a point above the west face of the chalk pit, a good view is obtained of the profile of the country to the east. In the foreground the dip-slope is subdivided by Dean Bottom, a strike valley which, like the Headley valley, may well have originated beyond a former margin of the Eocene outcrop. This separates Clandon Downs from the higher parts of the Chalk plateau. Beyond its head the dip-slope is unbroken but shows two distinct facets (Fig. 4). The lower, more steeply sloping, portion, largely in arable land, is evidently a close approximation to the sub-Eocene plane. Southwards this gives place to the 'high plateau' surface, largely wooded, which bevels the escarpment. Of this we see more as we continue our route southward: the surface at first rises steadily, but above 500 feet it flattens where we reach the summit-plane of the Downs. As we rise a wide view opens out northward over the London Basin; it is best obtained from near the point 045501, where a gravelled track diverges leftward from the road. The prospect extends across the Thames Valley to the Chiltern Hills, with the flat summit of St George's Hill, Weybridge, prominent in the foreground. From such a vantage point the well-wooded character of the London Basin, with its abundant hedge-row timber in addition to wide stretches of woodland and coppice, is readily appreciated.

The summit plateau which we now cross on the way to Newlands Corner is covered with close-grown Chalk scrub and woodland. The northern edge of the plateau is on bare Chalk, but beyond the Newlands Corner Hotel we pass on to a sheet of gravelly deposits. These are distinguished by the Geological Survey as the 'Netley Heath Deposits'; from masses of ironstone included in them marine Pliocene fossils have been obtained and there is no doubt that we are dealing with the same series of sands and gravels as occur at Headley Heath at about the same elevation, though the deposits have been much disturbed by 'freeze and thaw' and

sludging during the arctic phases of Pleistocene times, as well as
by the solution of the underlying Chalk. These disturbances have
confused and reconstructed the original deposits but they here
form a fairly thick and continuous mantle on the crest of the Chalk
escarpment between about 550 and 650 feet O.D. The doubts
which have been felt concerning their precise age and the amount
of disturbance they have since suffered leave quite unaltered the
main physiographic conclusion which their presence justifies.
Since relics of marine deposits occur here and elsewhere at or near
the crest of the Chalk escarpment at a level of about 600 feet the
landscape as we see it has been evolved during and after the elevation of the old sea-floor; the rivers of the area cannot have begun
to flow until the sheet of marine deposits was raised above sea-
level. Northwards the wide trough of the London Basin has been
excavated since this time and the southward view from Newlands
Corner bears equally evident witness of the contemporary excavation of the Wealden vales.

This view is best seen by turning a few yards right off the main
road opposite 'The Barn'. Below us lies the Vale of Holmesdale
with the broad dip-slope of the Leith Hill range on its far side. As
its crest-line falls westward towards the Wey, our view extends
across it to the South Downs, from Rackham Hill to a point west
of the Arun Gap. Closer at hand to the south-west we see the
scarp of the Hythe Beds resuming its course beyond the Wey at
Hascombe Beeches while behind rise the high bastions of Hindhead (marked by its radar aerials) and Blackdown. These high
points, together with the crest of the Leith Hill range, rise above
the level of the Pliocene marine flat on which we are standing and
must have formed part of the contemporary land surface in Pliocene times. The excavation of Holmesdale and the wider lowland
of the Weald Clay has left them standing in relief together with the
Chalk escarpment.

THE CHALK ESCARPMENT AND THE HOLMESDALE

Descend the escarpment by a rough gravelled track which goes
down leftwards from near our view-point. It crosses coarse Chalk
grassland and open scrub, with yew and juniper. As the path
descends fine views open out along the face of the escarpment,
westward to the Hog's Back and eastward towards Dorking. A

number of obvious 'terrace ways' will be noted on the face of the
scarp above the track, suggesting that a prehistoric route climbed
to the summit here. At the foot of the steeper part of the slope the
track bends sharp right at the point where it crosses the line of a
bridleway marking the upper limit of cultivation, the usual line of
the 'Pilgrims' Way' (p. 124). The cutting into which the track now
descends gives roadside exposures of the lower beds of the Chalk
and of chalk-rubble or 'coombe-rock'—sludge which mantled the
scarp-face during the 'freeze and thaw' conditions of Pleistocene
times.

Where the track resumes a north–south line turn back (right)
into an old chalk pit. This exposes the upper beds of the Lower
Chalk capped by the hard nodular beds at the base of the succeeding Middle Chalk. The section is now much obscured by
talus, but it is possible to verify that the rocks are dipping northwards at a steep angle, near 30°. By reason of the high dip the
outcrops of the Upper Greensand and Gault are rendered very
narrow. When we leave the pit and resume our southward route,
the low feature made by the Upper Greensand may be seen east of
the lane opposite the point where the track to Newbarn leaves it.
This track here runs on the Gault and water is held up on its outcrop in the field just south of the lane junction. The outcrop is
exceedingly narrow, however, and as we continue down the lane
the section shown in the banks reveals a thick layer of chalk-
rubble (coombe-rock) which helps to obscure further the normal
features of the clay outcrop. At the next lane junction where a track
leads east (about 047485) we have clearly passed on to the outcrop
of the Folkestone Sands; these are well exposed in a large pit west
of the lane about 100 yards further south. Here the northward dip
is less (about 15°): care must be taken not to confuse the northerly
inclination of the true bedding with the steeply inclined false—
or current-bedding—which, as is usual in the Folkestone Sands,
is inclined steeply towards the south or south-east.

It will be seen that in the short traverse from the chalk pit we
have crossed the outcrops of part of the Lower Chalk, the Upper
Greensand, the Gault and part of the Folkestone Sands. If we
credit the four formations with their maximum known thickness
for the district a thickness of some 700 feet of strata is crossed in
about 2,000 feet (reckoned to the base of the Folkestone Sands).

On flat ground this would imply a dip of about 20°, which is probably near the average figure for the zone of steep dip though, as we have seen, it is higher on its northern and lower on its southern edge. The structure is indicated in the section (Fig. 27) which, having only a small vertical exaggeration, well expresses the comparative insignificance of the local land forms compared with the great fold from which they have been sculptured. It is possible that the attenuation of the outcrops in the zone of steep dip is assisted by faulting, for the Hog's Back thrust which accompanies the northern limit of the great fold sets in along the foot of the escarpment only three miles to the west. In this neighbourhood no line of fracture can be clearly demonstrated, however; if present it probably lies within the Gault outcrop. Whether or not faulting is present, the effect of the steep dip is to reduce the true Gault vale to almost insignificant width, for the sandy country of the Folkestone Beds almost adjoins the foot of the Chalk escarpment.

DIVERSION TO THE 'SILENT POOL'

If time permits we may here turn eastward along the side lane to make an interesting detour of about 2 miles back to Albury. The lane at first runs on the Folkestone Sands but a little beyond a cottage on the right (053485) it passes on to the narrow outcrop of the Gault which is exposed still further to the east in a brickworks. On reaching the main road continue eastward for 300 yards and then turn left along the private road leading to Sherbourne Farm and the 'Silent Pool'. This is the upper of two ponds fed by a powerful chalk spring at its head. The pool lies athwart the boundary of the Upper Greensand and the Lower Chalk, while the lower pond is on the Gault. This is the only well-marked scarp-foot spring between Guildford and Dorking. Note the miniature coombe-like head of the pool surrounded by high banks of chalk. This feature must have been produced largely by solution and invites comparison with the larger spring-coombes, now dry, which break the line of the scarp a little farther east.

On rejoining the road, turn left and then right on the main road to Albury, but after crossing the Tillingbourne avoid the Albury road on the right and continue uphill on the road to Farley Green. Leave this at the first gate on the right and follow the cart-

track westward along the south slope of the Tillingbourne valley
to Blackheath Lane west of Albury Church.

THE PEASEMARSH ANTICLINE AT ALBURY

On a first visit to the area a clearer idea of the structure of the
ground is probably got by deferring the detour just described and
completing a north–south traverse of the Tillingbourne valley. If
this is preferred, continue southward from the lane corner
(047483) past Water Lane Farm to the main road. The lane follows the line of a small obsequent valley which breaches the
southward facing escarpment of the Folkestone Sands prominent
above the road in Weston Wood. At the base of the Folkestone
Sands the Bargate Stone should emerge but its outcrop is dis-
continuous. It is present in force only 200 yards to the west where
we cross its outcrop later, but it has not been detected where our
lane crosses its line, nor along the southern edge of Weston Wood.

Turn left in the main road and descend across the Tillingbourne
to Albury village, noting signs of a small gravel terrace in the
road cutting on the right. Beyond the bridge turn right along
Blackheath Lane which climbs the south slope of the valley, soon
passing into a deep cutting. This exposes the upper part of the
Hythe Beds, pale coloured sands with bands of nodular cherty
sandstone, and above it the Bargate Stone—a coarse calcareous
sandstone, strongly-bedded. We have now passed over the crest
of the Peasemarsh anticline and the beds dip southward at 2–3°:
here again we must be careful to distinguish the true from the
false-bedding, for the latter dips at a much steeper angle (about
20°) towards the south-east and can easily mislead us as to the
amount of the dip. Note too that the calcareous stone weathers
down near the surface into a deep loamy soil. At the top of the hill
enter the fenced track on the right which affords us a view northward along the route we have followed from Newlands Corner.
The knoll westward of us (Birget Hill) is capped by Folkestone
Sands and they can be reconstructed in imagination arching over
the valley and coming down to ground on the north side of the
anticline in Weston Wood.

Return northward by Blackheath Lane to Albury. (The detour
to the 'Silent Pool' may here be made, if desired, in the reverse
direction, by turning right past Albury Church.) Turn left in the

main road and then right up Guildford Lane just beyond the Water Lane turning. The banks of Guildford Lane at once present an excellent section in the Hythe Beds succeeded above by the Bargate Stone which is traceable in the lane banks for about 300 yards. The beds seen in the cutting appear not far from horizontal since we are here near to the crest of the anticline and the road section is, in any case, only slightly oblique to the direction of strike.

ST MARTHA'S HILL

As the lane climbs we soon pass on to Folkestone Sands; where it veers right by a clump of pines continue forward over open heath by the track which climbs westward to the summit of St Martha's Hill (578 feet). The hill is built of Folkestone Sands which here rise in nearly their full thickness above the Bargate Beds. The latter form a ledge above the steep northern slope of the Tillingbourne valley. But it is important to notice that the height and prominence of the hill reflect the structure of the ground: the base of the Folkestone Sands, below 300 feet O.D. at Weston Wood, is fully 100 feet higher below St Martha's summit, since we are here closer to the crest of the Peasemarsh anticline.

The summit gives us a prospect of the Weald by way of the broad breach made by the Wey in the Hythe Beds escarpment. From a point beyond the pinewood north of the church, the view in the opposite direction extends across the Chalk escarpment, here declining in height westward as the dip increases, into and sometimes across the western end of the London Basin. Even when the more distant views are obscured, however, there is much to be studied in the foreground. The anticlinal vale of Albury is clearly seen and we can trace the course of a further subsequent stream running parallel with the Tillingbourne south of Albury Heath but swinging north to join its neighbour near Postford House. It is this stream which collects most of the drainage of the Hythe dip-slope and its valley affords a route for the southerly diversion made by the railway to avoid Albury Park (see note on drainage below).

THE 'PILGRIMS' WAY'

From the summit of St Martha's we may also give attention to the problem of the several old east–west tracks which traverse this

area. Tradition attaches the name 'Pilgrims' Way' to the track
which crosses the summit and there is evidence that the church,
dedicated to St Martha, and All Holy Martyrs, itself became a
place of pilgrimage and was no doubt visited also by pilgrims *en
route* to Canterbury. It is probable, however, that St Martha's
was a parish church in the eleventh century before the days of
pilgrimage. It later became connected with Newark Priory in the
neighbouring parish of Send: this was founded in memory of
Thomas Becket and no doubt the pilgrimage association at St
Martha's arose from this fact. The supposed relation of St Martha's
and its track with Bunyan and his *Pilgrim's Progress* is ingenious
rather than convincing, since there is no positive evidence whatever to support it. The history and geography of the local 'old
roads' is, in fact, confused rather than clarified by the rather
disputable lore of pilgrimage. We can best straighten a tangled
story by recalling that, in general, throughout the northern Weald,
we find signs of one or more of these ancient trackways following
respectively the crest of the Downs, their southern foot and the
northern edge of the Lower Greensand outcrop. All three are
represented on the ground before us, the first by the scarp-crest
track which is continuous from Pewley Down, Guildford to Denbies (p. 107), the second below Pewley Down and again below
Albury Downs, and the third by the track which follows the north
side of the Chantries ridge west of St Martha's, and on past
Tyting Farm north of the hill. Farther east in Surrey (p. 81)
and throughout Kent the scarp-foot track is the most plainly
marked and continuous and generally carries the title 'Pilgrims'
Way', but there is little doubt, in fact, that it is a prehistoric trackway dating probably from Neolithic times. Though its continuity
is broken between Guildford and Dorking, signs of it can be found
in places and here too it probably discharged its prehistoric roles,
taking rank as the oldest of the three trackways we have mentioned.
Its attraction was that it afforded a readily traceable way through
country then almost uniformly covered with dense forest. Whether
or not the steep slopes of the Chalk escarpment were in part clear
of trees, the scarp-face must have been an indispensable 'direction-
finder' in conditions of poor visibility or failing light. The 'Old
Road' certainly retained its importance during the earlier Medieval
centuries, but as traffic increased and the country was cleared the

'Greensand route' locally offered a preferable alternative. In the
Guildford district it lay barely quarter of a mile from the base
of the Chalk escarpment, itself less clearly marked than usual
owing to the high dip. Therefore, for reasons plainly implied in
the geological structure, the Greensand route here naturally took
the place of the scarp-foot track, following dry ground but remaining within easy sight and reach of the Chalk across the narrowed
furrow of Holmesdale. The alternative route via St Martha's summit merely gave access to the church whether for the normal purposes of the parish or the occasional needs of pilgrims. The
Pilgrims' Way of tradition adopts the Greensand route as far as
Gomshall, beyond which it climbs Hackhurst Downs, and follows
the summit track for some distance before descending to cross
the Mole and resume its normal scarp-foot line. The Wey crossing of the Greensand route is supposed to have been below St
Catherine's Chapel which stands on a bluff of Folkestone Sand
above the west bank of the river. We have, in fact, no positive
evidence of a ford here: the 'shallow ford' recalled in the name
'Shalford' must have been located about half a mile to the south.

ST MARTHA'S TO GUILDFORD

On leaving St Martha's summit descend westward to the road
(Halfpenny Lane). Turn left, and in about 30 yards note a footpath on the right. Before taking this path follow the road downhill
southward for a short distance where the Bargate Stone will be
found well exposed in the lane bank, with the coarse and pebbly
basal beds of the Folkestone Sands above it exposed nearby. On
returning to the footpath fork right almost at once; the path descends through woodland and is continued by a fenced track across
arable fields, climbing to the escarpment crest at Pewley Down.
Here we again cross the narrow Holmesdale furrow, the slope on
the left being in sand and that on the right in chalk with scant
trace of the Gault between them. From Pewley Down we obtain
a good view of the gravel-covered inlier of Weald Clay brought
up by the Peasemarsh anticline athwart the Wey between Guildford and Godalming. The plateau made by the Bargate Beds
around Godalming is well seen, with the Wey incised in a narrow
valley within it before making its exit into the little Peasemarsh
lowland. When our track comes out on the road at Pewley Hill

the view opens up once more northward over the London Basin. The road descends steeply into the Wey Gap and enables us to appreciate the site of the town.

Guildford is one of the few gap-towns which really lies in its gap: it had filled it so completely by the time of the coming of the railway that the latter was forced to tunnel through the Chalk south of the station. Nevertheless it was as a ford and later a bridge on an east–west route that the site gained its first significance: the route southward through the gap for long led only into the Wealden forest with its thin scatter of settlements.

To reach the station turn right along Chapel Street (opposite the castle ruins) and right again after crossing the river bridge at the lower end of High Street.

Note on the structure and drainage of the Lower Greensand area

Some supplementary suggestions on the physiography of the area may be of assistance to those concerned with more advanced study. We have outlined in general terms the structure of the country south of the Downs, but close study of the geological map at once suggests certain problems. In the first place it should be noted that the discontinuity in the outcrop of the Bargate Beds is less marked than the map suggests; the ground was mapped thirty years ago and fresh evidence has since come to hand. The true Bargate Stone is locally absent at the outcrop owing to decalcification of the beds, which renders them difficult, in some cases, to distinguish from the Hythe Beds below them. J. F. Kirkaldy * has shown that they are in fact present locally at points where they have not been mapped around the outlier of Folkestone Sands at Blackheath south of Albury. It is possible, indeed, that, if exposures were adequate, complete continuity might be shown, as in the Godalming country to the west. Nevertheless there is no doubt that the beds vary considerably in thickness from place to place; local uplift of the sea-floor brought them within reach of current scour before the Folkestone Beds were laid down. There is, in fact, a minor break or unconformity at the base of the Folkestone Sands.

If, therefore, we seek for a datum horizon by means of which we can elucidate the structure in detail, the best for the purpose is

* 'The Sandgate Beds of the Western Weald', *Proc. Geol. Assoc.* Vol. 44 (1933), p. 270.

the base of the Folkestone Sands. To the north of Albury, on the north side of the anticlinal axis, it lies below 300 feet, but southwards, on the flanks of Albury Warren, it is somewhat higher. To the east of this line the pitch of the fold carries it down below 250 feet; westward on the south crop, it rises to above 300 feet, while on the north crop, below St Martha's, it rises as high as 400 feet, dropping westwards again to about 350 feet along the Chantries ridge. These facts make clear the local form of the Peasemarsh anticline; like most of the Wealden folds it is notably asymmetrical, with its axis only a short distance south of St Martha's crest where the base of the Folkestone Sands may have reached an elevation of 500 feet or more relative to present Ordnance Datum. Farther west the Peasemarsh fold may be regarded as independent of the Hog's Back monocline, for its crest, passing through Crooksbury Hill and Compton, lies a full 1½ miles south of the Chalk escarpment. But it converges on the escarpment line eastwards and near Albury its northern flank is virtually coincident with the great monoclinal line (Fig. 27). South of the anticlinal axis a gentler synclinal feature follows a parallel line through Tilford and Blackheath.

These structural considerations become important in any attempt to trace the evolution of the drainage system. As was first clearly pointed out by H. Bury (*Quart. Jour. Geol. Soc.*, 66, 1910) the drainage of this area cannot be regarded as simply derived from the initial drainage system set up following the Wealden folding. It shows, on the contrary, many signs of having been *superimposed*, and it is now clearer than when Bury wrote that it cannot have been initiated until after the emergence of the Pliocene sea-floor and must, in fact, have been superimposed from the sheet of Pliocene deposits spread across the worn-down surface of the earlier folds. It is, in fact, in its first major cycle of erosion, at the beginning of which we have evidence of a number of independent consequent streams flowing northwards to the Thames. West of Guildford no fewer than four of these streams, including the ancestor of the Blackwater, traversed the emergent plane northwards across the line of the present Chalk escarpment. East of the Wey only one such stream is clearly evidenced, lying roughly halfway between the Wey and the Mole, its line represented today by the Peaslake stream on the dip-slope of the Hythe

Beds and the major dry valley which drains northward from the col on Netley Heath at Gravelhill Gate (089494). This initial family of consequent streams has been largely integrated by river-capture by the ordinary process of 'adaptation to structure'—i.e. the growth of subsequent streams. It is in connexion with this process that a full knowledge of the structure and of the outcrop geology of the 'hill-top plain' beneath the Pliocene deposits becomes important. In Fig. 28 this is reconstructed, together with the lines of the original consequent rivers. The Wey has proved the successful member of the series and it has captured the head-streams of its neighbours through the activity of subsequent branches extending themselves headwards in structurally favourable positions. On the west, the Godalming Wey, a subsequent branch of the consequent trunk draining from the Weald Clay to the south, has effected a series of captures of which the latest and most clearly marked is the beheading of the Blackwater south of Aldershot. The several stages of integration of the drainage are shown in Fig. 28, which indicate further that the successful subsequent tributary follows the line of the Tilford syncline, which must have preserved a Gault filling over a considerable area at the 600-foot level. The states of integration of the drainage east of the Wey can be studied within the limits of Sheet 51/04 used for the above excursion. The Peaslake Stream above Pursers Farm (089455) retains the line of the original Netley Heath consequent stream. This line has been broken by the activity of two parallel subsequent streams. With the Tillingbourne, following the Peasemarsh anticline, we are already familiar, but the map indicates that the Peaslake stream below Pursers Farm assumes a subsequent direction through Brook, roughly on the line of the Blackheath syncline. Today the stream swings northwards to join the Tillingbourne west of Albury, but its line through Brook is continued by that of the valley south of Blackheath, separated at its head from the Brook stream by a broad col with its floor just about 300 feet.

The suggested sequence of drainage development indicated in Fig. 28 shows that in the earlier stages the Tillingbourne and the Brook stream appear to have developed by headward extension at about the same rate. The latter must for a time have felt the advantage of excavating in Gault preserved in the Blackheath syncline. The Tillingbourne could have enjoyed no similar advantage

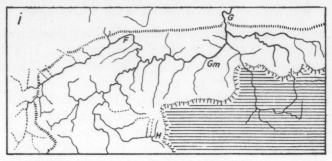

(i) The Wealden branches of the Wey at the present day.
⟨ᴍᴜᴜᴜ⟩ Chalk escarpment. ⟨ᴛᴛᴛᴛ⟩ Hythe Beds escarpment. ⟨∿⟩ Dry valleys.
⟨≡⟩ Weald Clay. G, Guildford (the Chalk gap). F, Farnham.
Gm, Godalming. H, Haslemere.

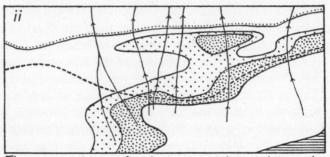

The same area showing inferred outcrops and drainage lines on the
emerged Pliocene platform. ---- = Inferred Pliocene shore-line.
⟨∴⟩ Tertiary margin. ⟨∴⟩ Gault. ⟨∷⟩ Folkestone Beds, Bargate
Beds. ⟨≡⟩ Weald Clay. Chalk and Malmstone together, and the
Hythe Beds, left unshaded.

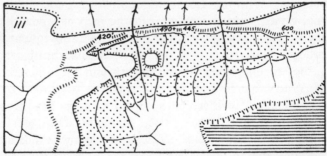

(iii) Inferred outcrops and drainage lines after the deepening of the
main valleys to about the 400 ft contour. These lines show development of subsequent streams and the earlier stream captures.
⟨∴⟩ Tertiary margin. ⟨ᴍᴜᴜᴜ⟩ Chalk escarpment. ⟨∿⟩ Escarpment of
the Malmstone. ⟨ᴛᴛᴛᴛ⟩ Hythe Beds escarpment. ⟨∴⟩ Gault,
Folkestone Beds, etc. together. ⟨≡⟩ Weald Clay.

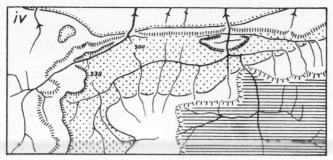

(iv) Inferred outcrops and drainage lines after deepening of the main valleys to about the 300 ft contour. Symbols as in Map iii, with the addition of ⟨⟨⟨⟨⟨, representing the newly formed escarpment of the Bargate Beds at the centre of the Peasemarsh anticline.

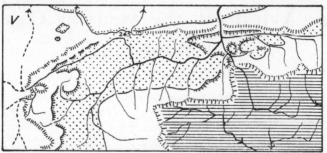

(v) Inferred outcrops and drainage lines at the time of the Farnham capture. Symbols as in Maps iii and iv.

Fig. 28.   A series of maps showing the evolution of the Wey drainage in post-Pliocene times (after D. L. Linton)

on the crest of the Peasemarsh anticline and probably originated at the foot of the Chalk escarpment in the true 'Holmesdale position' on Gault or Lower Chalk, though of course on a line slightly farther south, because at a higher level, than the present Holmesdale furrow. By the joint action of the two subsequent streams the Netley Heath consequent line was doubly broken. At a later stage the Tillingbourne outran and outflanked its neighbour, possessing itself of the drainage of the Hythe Beds dip-slope north of Leith Hill, some of which drained earlier to the Mole. As valley deepening progressed throughout the area, the clay core of the Peasemarsh fold became exposed; Fig. 28 (iv) indicates the beginning of a subsequent stream within it. In Fig. 28 (v) the Tillingbourne is

10

represented as forsaking its former slightly more northerly route near Albury and inheriting the anticline crest-line, while a south bank tributary was able to divert the Brook stream above Farley Green.

The reconstruction inevitably leaves some points in doubt; the surviving evidence is not sufficiently full to render the complete course of events clear. The type of reasoning employed, however, is applicable not only in this region but in all areas of strongly belted structure with a '*trellised*' drainage. It is thus a useful exercise in applying the principles of geomorphology in ground readily accessible of which the structures and general physical history are known.

6. Aylesford, the Medway Gap and Maidstone

MAPS: One-inch Ordnance Survey New Popular, Sheet 172
    1 : 25,000 Ordnance Survey, Sheets 51/75 and 51/76
    Geological Survey One-inch, Sheets 272 (Chatham) and 288 (Maidstone) (the latter in preparation)

WALKING DISTANCE for the whole route as given: 12 miles, admitting of various reductions

ACCESS: Train from Victoria to East Malling, returning from Maidstone East (hourly service throughout the day), or train from Charing Cross or London Bridge to Aylesford, returning from Maidstone West

This excursion will enable the geographer to compare the Medway gap in the North Downs with the gaps of two other Wealden rivers, the Darent and the Mole. The middle Medway basin has been greatly exploited for its mineral resources, extensive workings occurring in the Chalk, the Gault, the Lower Greensand, and in the river deposits overlying these rocks. These exposures in the rocks are of great value to the student in elucidating the geology of the area. Industrial development, which has impressed itself indelibly on every Medway landscape, has at all times been favoured by the facility of water transport along the tidal river. An interesting aspect of the agriculture of the Medway area is the extensive cultivation of the land over the whole of the Hythe Beds outcrop. In this particular sector of the northern Weald the sand and stone of the Hythe Beds are distinctly calcareous and the proportion of siliceous chert is small. On weathering this rock material yields deep loamy soils which are among the best in the country for the cultivation of hops and fruit.

The excursion in the Aylesford district admits of several variations as to walking distance and subjects of study. To follow the whole of the route described, with its several diversions, would be quite a strenuous day's work. The reader would do well therefore to study the route beforehand with the aid of the maps and decide on his points of arrival and departure by train, and at what stages he might make use of bus services within the area. The itinerary as described begins at East Malling station on the Victoria to Maidstone line. Walking distance in the country between East Malling and Aylesford is only 3 miles, but the study of its many points of interest might occupy more time than could be allowed if the start is made after mid-morning. In such case the reader may travel by train to Aylesford, using the North Kent line via Strood and the Medway valley. The most important part of the whole route is the walk from Aylesford to Blue Bell Hill, the well-known summit of the North Downs at the entrance of the Medway gap. The journey back from this point to Maidstone may be made in any of several ways, including stages by bus if desired. Suggestions for these variants are given in the itinerary. The train journey from Maidstone to London may be either on the North Kent line or the line to Victoria according to the route chosen for the outward journey.

EAST MALLING TO AYLESFORD

At East Malling Halt the railway runs along an embankment which in places commands a view over the village and its surrounding orchards towards the escarpment of the North Downs. From the railway platform this view is partly obstructed by tall trees but it may be studied from one or two vantage points on the higher ground to the south.

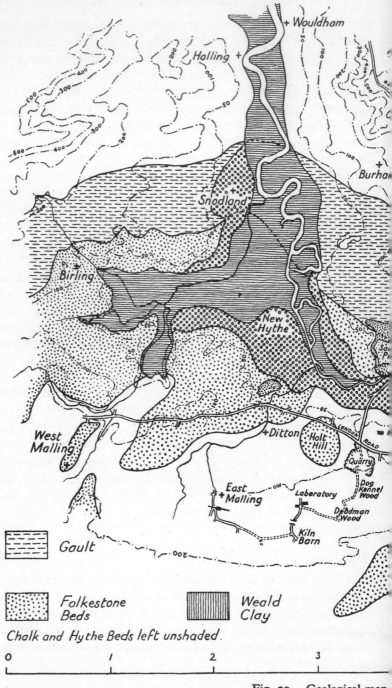

Gault

Folkestone Beds   Weald Clay

Chalk and Hythe Beds left unshaded.

0   1   2   3

Fig. 29.   Geological map

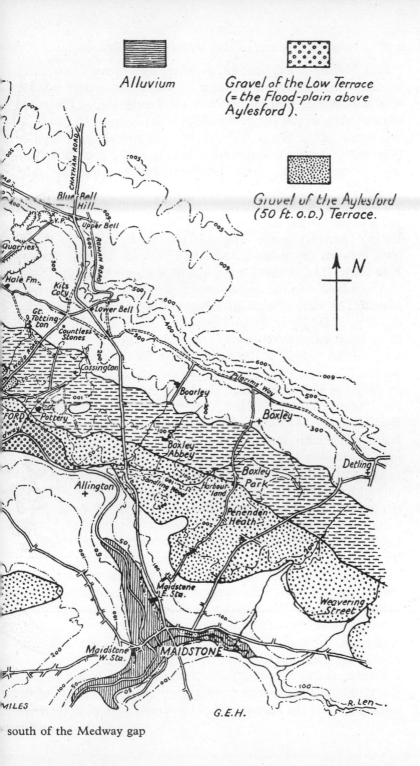

Alluvium

Gravel of the Low Terrace
(= the Flood-plain above
Aylesford).

Gravel of the Aylesford
(50 ft. o.d.) Terrace.

N

CHATHAM ROAD

Blue Bell
Hill
V.P.
Upper Bell
ROMAN ROAD

Quarries

Hale Fm.

Kits
Coty
Gt.
Totting-
ton
Countless
Stones

Lower Bell

Cossington

FORD
Pottery
dway

Boarley

Pilgrims' Way

Boxley

Detling

Boxley
Abbey

Allington

Sandling Wd.

Boxley
Park

Harbour-
land

Penenden
Heath

Maidstone
E. Sta.

Weavering
Street

Maidstone
W. Sta.

MAIDSTONE

MILES

R. Len

G.E.H.

south of the Medway gap

East Malling is a typical village of the Greensand hill country of mid-Kent. Observe its situation on the hillside and its relation to a small stream flowing northward down the slope. The stone used in many of the village buildings is the Kentish 'ragstone', a constituent of the Hythe Beds which cover this elevated country (Fig. 29). Old stone quarries are numerous in the district. Extensive workings in the Hythe Beds may be inspected later near Aylesford.

From East Malling Halt take the left branch of the road just south of the railway and follow it as far as the house called 'The Rocks'. Continue in the same direction, ESE, along the cinder track between the orchards and then follow the footpath towards Kiln Barn. The orchard trees almost everywhere obstruct the northward view so that good vantage points have to be carefully sought. The view extends first over a mile or more of the even dip-slope of the Hythe Beds. This surface is almost wholly utilized as orchard and market garden land. The portion immediately north of the railway is the estate of the East Malling Research Station. The only upstanding feature on the surface is Holt Hill, an outlier of Folkestone Sand on the Hythe Beds. At the foot of the dip-slope, in the middle distance of the view, is the industrial riverside below Aylesford. The low-lying land of the Medway flood-plain extends into the gap in the Chalk downs, the northern limit of the view.

The true river gap in the Chalk, in the sense of a steep-sided valley such as we are familiar with in the Mole and the Darent, is not seen in this prospect of the middle Medway basin. What we perceive in the distant part of the landscape is the Chalk escarpment on the east and the west sides of the Medway in two converging alignments. The eastern range of the scarp begins to sweep more rapidly northward at Blue Bell Hill, while the western range, maintaining for many miles a north-easterly direction, disappears behind it. This is where the actual river gap is a wide but steep-sided Chalk valley running NE from Halling down to Rochester. A glance at the map will show clearly the convergence of the two lines of the escarpment towards the Medway gap.

Leaving the view-point, continue on the footpath to Kiln Barn and turn left into the road to pass again to the north side of the railway line. At the Laboratory of the Research Station turn east along a track beside the buildings and follow this to the corner of Deadman Wood. Here turn NE into the footpath through the wood, continue to the southern boundary of the next piece of orchard land and turn eastward again to the track which runs along the outside of Dog Kennel Wood. The vegetation of these two small areas of woodland is of some interest. It consists of a robust growth of mixed timber in the form of *coppice-with-standards* (p. 45). The standard trees are invariably oaks but the coppiced wood is very mixed. Chestnut is the dominant species, with hazel almost as plentiful in places. Other species present are hornbeam, ash, maple, birch and occasionally oak. Chestnut flourishes on light loamy or sandy soils and its abundance and vigour are indications of soil fertility. It is the most useful of all the coppiced timbers and has been extensively planted in the higher grade woodlands in southern Britain. In this fertile district chestnut was formerly used for hop poles. Deadman Wood and Dog Kennel Wood are in different phases of the coppicing cycle and the two should be compared.

Continue on the track northward past a large wood yard on the right and the old overgrown parts of Preston Hall Quarries on the left. The section of the Hythe Beds exposed in these quarries was recorded in Topley's *Geology of the Weald* in 1875. The northern end was re-opened in recent times and is being worked for road stone. The entrance is on the main road near the British Legion Village, and permission to enter the quarries may be obtained on the site.

The quarry exposes in all some 30 feet of Hythe Beds typical of the mid-Kent facies (the full thickness on this meridian is reckoned to be about 100 feet). The material is a succession of beds of hard, sandy limestone ('rag'), varying from a few inches to 2 feet or more in thickness, separated by layers of 'hassock' (sand or soft stone), also calcareous to some extent and similarly varying in thickness. There are occasional thin beds of hard, siliceous 'chert', a material which farther west becomes an important element in the Hythe Beds. Of special interest to the geographer is the soil profile above the unaltered rock strata. The soil is seen to be derived from the weathering of the calcareous sandstone, since it grades down into it without a break. Near the surface the soil is a deep reddish brown loam containing fragments of rock ('pinnock'). Elsewhere on the Hythe Beds there are other kinds of highly fertile soil, notably deposited 'brickearths', but the fertility of the area around Maidstone depends largely on the well textured and chemically efficient loams derived from the weathering of ragstone and hassock.

From Preston Hall Quarries, cross the London Road to the lane going down to the Medway at Aylesford. This approach introduces us to important features of the river valley. At Preston Hall Farm the road descends a small bluff to a low plain bordering the river. We shall later see something of the great extent of this surface over the valley floor, and observe also that it is the surface of a thick spread of alluvial gravel. It is in fact an old flood-plain of the Medway. The river is now deeply entrenched in it, and half a mile or so downstream of Aylesford a more recently formed flood-plain has been laid down at a slightly lower level, the gravel plain there forming a true *terrace* on either side of it (p. 29 and Fig. 11).

THE ENVIRONS OF AYLESFORD

On reaching Aylesford Bridge it will be observed that the village on the far side is built partly on the low gravel plain and partly on ground rising to some 30 feet above it (about 50 feet O.D.). We shall find that this higher ground is also a level surface of considerable extent (an older river terrace) ending abruptly at the river bank. The sharp drop to the river represents a true river cliff, but the slope has been modified in the course of building the village.

Before crossing the bridge we may examine the river channel, but it is only possible to do this at low tide. The Medway is tidal as far inland as Allington, a mile and a half upstream of Aylesford. At Aylesford Bridge there is a tidal range of 11 feet, and when the level of water is low enough it is possible to see layers of ragstone exposed in the bed of the river. Exposed is perhaps hardly the word, for the channel is lined with black mud polluted with industrial wastes from riverside factories. Nevertheless, the ragstone appears as distinct ridges, especially along the right bank of the channel. A short walk along the towpath on the left bank will enable the observer to see that the high ground of the old river cliff above the wharf of the Aylesford Sand Company consists of the overlying Folkestone Sands.

Returning to the bridge and looking upstream the great expanse of the low gravel plain may be seen. The eastern part of Aylesford village which we now enter is built on this surface and we follow its margin against the sharply rising mass of Folkestone Sand at the side of the Chatham road ('Wood Road'), noting that along this line a stream comes down from the Chalk hills above. About 350 yards along Wood Road turn left into the entrance of the Aylesford Sand Company's large pit. This old working is responsible for the removal of a great part of the Aylesford 50-foot terrace, whose level surface can be appreciated as the eye follows the long line of the working face. Examining a portion of the north face of the pit 200 yards or so from the entrance, we see current-bedded ochreous sand with layers of hard, irony sandstone, all typical of the Folkestone Beds. The sands are overlain with 10 to 15 feet of Medway gravel composed of flint and Lower Greensand stone in a sandy or silty matrix. The gravel rests somewhat irregularly on the underlying sand, but its upper surface is uniformly flat. It is possible to climb to the top of the face in this disused part of the pit and to view the cultivated surface of the terrace, observing its great extent. Aylesford Church and other buildings of the village are seen to occupy the southern margin of the flat. It is interesting to see how cultivation has been restored over the levelled floor of the old parts of the pit.

Immediately to the north of the entrance of the sand pit Wood Road itself rises to the level of the terrace surface. We may continue along this road towards the Chalk scarp (p. 141), but if time permits a diversion eastwards to Aylesford Pottery is worth while.

DIVERSION TO THE GAULT SECTION AT AYLESFORD POTTERY

Turn right from Wood Road just beyond the Old Mill House and follow the road which descends again to the lower gravel plain. The view southward from the slope carries the eye across the flat land of the valley floor to Preston Hall and the high ridge of the Hythe Beds beyond it. Along the lower stretch of this road it will be clear from the clay soil in the adjoining fields that the land bordering the low gravel plain is on Gault. It should be remembered that the alignment of the outcrops is rather S of E, so that our easterly journey carries us up the sequence.

Time may permit a visit to the gravel workings and the gravel-washing plant which lie south of the road towards the river. Here the lower gravel deposits are worked to a depth determined by the sub-surface water-table (it will be noticed that all the worked-out pits contain standing water). Like the higher terrace deposit the lower gravel is composed of flint and sandstone in a variable matrix. The presence of flint in gravels lying far south of the Chalk, its parent rock, is indicative of the former southward extension of the Chalk over the Wealden area; the flint is a residuum of the denudation process. Needless to say, flint fragments and pebbles found in the lower (and therefore younger) river deposits have not come there direct from recently destroyed chalk, but have been derived from the destruction of higher and older river deposits one after the other in a long succession. It is relevant here to re-call that, in general, high-level gravels survive only in small, widely separated patches, while lower lying deposits are successively better preserved and more nearly continuous in their distribution.

Passing the bend in the road towards Pratling Street, enter by a gate the premises of the disused Aylesford Pottery (now the pro-perty of the London Brick Company). Continue eastward along a track through the overgrown part of the clay workings. In a short distance the track opens into a pit of impressive dimensions expos-ing weathered faces of bluish Gault clay surmounted by a layer of displaced Chalk. In this abandoned pit the weathering and erosion of clay may be profitably studied. The reader is warned, however, that because of the instability of the material it is dan-gerous to approach any nearly vertical face. In wet weather prac-tically all surfaces are impassable and there are treacherous mud-streams. When the clay is dry the higher parts of the north face may be reached quite safely and the section in the overlying chalky deposit examined. This material, though considerably dis-turbed, has probably not been far removed from its place of origin, for we are here quite close to the top of the Gault (a small outlier of Chalk *in situ* occupies the summit of the hill immediately E of the clay pit). It will be seen that the chalky deposit in the section incorporates some broken and weathered flints as well as sandy material. These are no doubt relics of 'scarp drift', itself incor-porating material derived from the chalk plateau.

It is possible to leave the pit by a footpath above the northern face and through a belt of woodland down to the farm road from Cossington. Over the lower ground in this vicinity there are no superficial deposits on the Gault and the soil is seen to consist essentially of the grey clay. In the 180 miles of its outcrop around the Weald the Gault is predominantly a belt of woodland and pasture, the soil being too heavy and wet for cultivation. For some miles east of the Medway, however, the soil of the Gault is exceptionally fertile, possibly because here the clay is more calcareous. Our traverse of the outcrop from the bottom of Cossington Lane to Great Tottington is almost wholly through orchards on this clay, first along the narrow lane running almost due N, then by a footpath turning NW just above Little Cossington (743600). The footpath crosses Wood Road, a point which may be reached by the alternative walk direct from Aylesford (p. 139).

THE SCARP-FOOT AND THE CHALK QUARRIES

In a short distance the footpath crossing Wood Road comes to a bridge over a copiously flowing stream, the same which lower down flows beside the street in Aylesford. The stream rises in a deep hollow just above the farm at Great Tottington. Unfortunately the emergence of the water from the base of the Chalk cannot be seen as it is beneath the surface of an artificially constructed basin, but the site is typical of the scarp-foot springs along this sector of the Chalk.

The footpath from Great Tottington to Hale Farm on the Burham road has been effaced, but the objective may be reached by following field boundaries. The ground is wholly on the drift-covered lower slopes of the Chalk, a section of which is admirably revealed in the large chalk pit immediately north of Hale Farm. The land is highly fertile and is almost entirely in arable cultivation. At the junction of the Burham road ('Pilgrims' Way') and the road to Eccles the lowest of the series of great chalk pits may be examined. The workings here are mainly in the Chalk Marl, the lowest division of the Chalk formation, but partly also in the Grey Chalk immediately above it. These beds, devoid of flint, and containing a natural admixture of clay, provide the ideal material for cement manufacture. They have been extensively worked both here at Burham and at Snodland on the other side of the Medway. The section shows a deposit of 'scarp drift' resting on the Chalk.

This deposit, increasing in thickness down the slope, incorporates materials derived from the Chalk plateau and from the scarp-face. These include flints containing Upper Chalk fossils, and pieces of sarsen stone originating in the Eocene (Woolwich Beds).

From the Burham road commence the ascent of the scarp by the track alongside the old quarries. The upper part of this once much used track has now become overgrown, but it is not difficult to penetrate the belt of scrub where the overhead electric power lines go up the steepest part of the slope. Emerging on the open sward near the edge of the highest of the quarries we may select a vantage point from which to view the Medway plain and its surrounding hills.

THE VIEW FROM BLUE BELL HILL

Westward in the middle distance of this magnificent landscape may be seen the great expanse of alluvial marshland between New Hythe, Leybourne and Halling. It is distinguished by its level surface, grass-covered and treeless, and by the sinuous tidal channel of the river within its boundaries. The alluvium is spread out over some $2\frac{1}{2}$ square miles of the Gault and Folkestone Sand outcrops, a layer of fine silt beneath which the whole of an older Medway valley floor lies buried. The deposition of alluvium in the seaward ends of the southern river valleys is the result of a geologically recent change in the relative levels of land and sea, equivalent in amount to a general lowering of the land surface to the extent of some 70 feet. The change in level has brought the sea tide far inland along the rivers, but the marine invasion has been accompanied by silt deposition in the valleys so that at all stages during the process an estuarine flood-plain has been maintained at high tide level. The marshland surface, as here in the Medway, is now for the most part protected from tidal floods by embankment of the river channels. The floods which at times cover the marshes and form a conspicuous element in this view of the Medway from Blue Bell Hill are caused by water from the surrounding high ground accumulating faster than it can be carried off with the ebbing tide. On the almost level alluvial plain the river has naturally developed a wandering course. Two of its large meander loops, locally known as the Horseshoe Bends, are to be seen in the direction of Snodland.

Beyond the Medway plain the westward view is bounded by the apparently converging crests of the North Downs and the Greensand range, with the broad Vale of Holmesdale between them. The scarp-face of the downs, sweeping south-westward away from the Medway gap at Halling, appears to end in the forward-standing salient of Wrotham Hill, but when visibility is at its best we may discern a far distant section of the downs standing a little farther to the south, culminating in the summit of Tandridge Hill 25 miles away, beyond the West Kent border. From that distant point we may follow eastward the dip-slope of the Greensand from the country south of Sevenoaks to that which forms the high ground west and east of Maidstone. Here, due south of our view-point, the Greensand appears as two parallel ranges, one with its crest falling away eastward from Mereworth to Maidstone, the other coming in from the east through Sutton Vallence and Cox Heath and disappearing behind the first. This division into two apparently separate ranges of the Greensand upland is brought about by the deep trench of the Medway which crosses the Greensand in a semi-circular sweep with the town of Maidstone situated midway along it. The curved course of the Greensand gap prevents a southward view through it into the Weald beyond.

The country running out from the foot of Blue Bell Hill immediately below us is the uniformly cultivated surface of the Lower Chalk and the Gault, extending down to the Medway flood-plain. The village of Burham on the scarp-foot road is one of a series of settlements along this zone of the downland. Its rows of drab cottages belong to the period over half a century ago when the cement industry of the Medway was rapidly growing. Cement manufacture on the Thames and Medway is now concentrated in a few factories of large size, but formerly works were situated at close intervals wherever the Chalk came near the navigable waterways. The now disused Burham works can be seen beside the river. The lake in the abandoned Gault pit immediately above it is a conspicuous feature in the landscape. Working cement factories may be seen at Snodland and Halling in the entrance of the Medway gap. Other factories which stand out in the view of the river valley are the large paper mills at Aylesford (New Hythe) and Snodland.

From the view-point high on the scarp-face it is possible to see Kits Coty House (745608) on the lower slopes of Blue Bell Hill. This is the chamber or dolmen of a megalithic structure, built of large masses of 'sarsen' sandstone. Remains of a number of these prehistoric works are distributed about the neighbourhood of the Medway gap. Some readers may wish to examine Kits Coty at closer quarters and also the so-called Countless Stones near by (744604). In order to do so they had best descend the hill by the main road, turning off at the signposted footpath about halfway down, then returning to the road by the Pilgrims' Way (p. 124).

DIVERSION TO VIEW THE MEDWAY GAP

For those who do not wish to continue field-work in the direction of Boxley (involving 4 miles further walking) the journey to Maidstone station may be made by bus from various points on the Maidstone–Chatham road (A.229). Buses on this route are frequent. This should allow time for a diversion from the top of Blue Bell Hill along Burham Common Road (on the scarp-crest) in order to see the narrower part of the Medway gap. From any open view-point above the village of Wouldham the observer is within 2 miles of the opposite side of the gap, where the Chalk escarpment sweeps gradually round to the north-easterly direction to form the bold slopes above Halling and Cuxton. The marsh-lands of the flood-plain are seen to form a belt fully half a mile wide along the valley floor, the tidal channel of the river within it widening downstream towards Rochester, where it may properly be called an estuary. A number of disused cement factories and abandoned chalk quarries mark the association of the valley villages with an earlier phase of the cement industry. Their place has been taken by other industries which, if not exploiting local materials, at least employ an established population and make use in one way or another of the land and water communications along the valley.

DESCENT OF BLUE BELL HILL

There are alternative ways of descending Blue Bell Hill; that of the main road with its diversion to Kits Coty has already been mentioned. The other is the old Blue Bell Hill road or Roman road, now a deserted byway. The modern road begins the descent at the Upper Bell public house, whereas the Roman road remains on the edge of the plateau for ¾ mile and goes down steeply into Lower Warren combe. The plateau about Blue Bell Hill is typically flat and covered with a variable thickness of Clay-with-flints. It carries a great amount of coppiced woodland, but the woods are interspersed with areas of cultivation centred on small and widely scattered farmsteads. Clay-with-flints is carried over from the plateau to parts of the scarp-face, and in places deeper deposits of this displaced material are held up on the slopes. In some of them large masses of sarsen stone are embedded. These are relics of a former Eocene cover which must have extended over the higher parts of the Chalk dip-slope.

BLUE BELL HILL TO MAIDSTONE VIA BOXLEY

A typical section of the 'Pilgrims' Way' (p. 124) runs eastward from the foot of Blue Bell Hill. It crosses the Maidstone–Chatham road at the point 752602, where the footpath comes down from Lower Warren Road. The walk via Boxley (alternative to the bus journey into Maidstone) begins at this point and follows the traditional line of the track for some distance.

On the north side of the track (754603), a short distance from the Maidstone Road, there is hidden in the scrub a standing slab of sarsen stone some 10 feet long by 6 feet high, with fragments of the same material lying about it. It is popularly known as the White Horse Stone and is probably the remains of another dolmen or burial chamber similar to Kits Coty.

Towards Boxley the vegetation of the slopes above the Pilgrims' Way is typical of the natural plant cover of the North Downs scarp-face. The open sward, consisting of grasses and a profusion of flowering plants, occurs mainly on the lower slopes. It is probably old grazing land upon which woody vegetation has not yet been established. There are signs everywhere of the invasion of the open sward by shrubs and trees, though the process has been checked to some extent by rabbit attack on the seedlings. Mature scrub, itself tending in places to become high forest dominated by beech and yew, occupies the higher parts of the scarp and forms masses and belts along old land boundaries. An irregular belt of scrub extends along the sides of the Pilgrims' Way. The vegetation of Boarley Scrubs and Tyland Scrubs is quite typical of this woody growth on the chalk.

From the site of the old Rifle Range above Boarley the observer may study the distant view of Maidstone and the surrounding hills of the Lower Greensand. The appearance of three distinct crest-lines of these hills is produced, as we have seen, and as the maps will show, by the semi-circular sweep of the Medway valley between them. Of Maidstone only the western outgrowth of the town on the slopes of the middle ridge is seen in the view; the heart of the town is concealed in the valley behind the Sandling ridge.

Near this point we may leave the Pilgrims' Way to descend to Boarley Farm. At the corner of the road there is a small chalk pit in which the soft Chalk Marl is exposed. The clay content of this lowest division of the Chalk should be noted. The large, prosperous farm at Boarley is situated on the spring-line, a fact which is demonstrated by the constant overflow of its pond. The Chalk water here, and at Boxley and Detling, is collected for the public water supply of Maidstone. At the collecting station just below Boarley Farm the attendant may be willing to explain the method of collecting and measuring the supply.

Spring-line farmsteads with hamlets have been noted at Great Tottington, Cossington and Boarley. The villages of Boxley, Detling and Thurnham are in the same zone; they received their water originally, if not from open springs, at least from shallow wells at the base of the Chalk. It will be observed that the nucleus of each of these sites is a little below the line of the Pilgrims' Way. Scarp-foot hamlets and villages do not occur in every sector of the North Downs, the Holmesdale settlements being usually on the Lower Greensand. East of the Medway, however, both lines of settlements are present, that of the scarp-foot being represented by Boxley, Detling, Thurnham and Upper Hollingbourne, while that of the Greensand is represented by Aylesford, Maidstone, Weavering Street, Bearsted and Lower Hollingbourne.

A footpath turns off the Boarley road immediately above the farm and passes through cultivated fields and orchards to Boxley. From this path the scarp-face may be viewed at a greater distance than from the Pilgrims' Way. The chalk pits at intervals along the scarp are sites of an old rural lime-burning industry. To the south

3a Coppice-with-standards, an artificial variant of the 'damp oakwood'. The example is on the Gault at Godstone, Surrey. The carpet of spring flowers occupies the ground around the oaks and the stools of the recently cut coppice trees

3b Woodland on Bagshot Sands, Esher Common, Surrey. The Durmast Oak is here associated with birch and pine. The undergrowth is locally dominated by bracken

the land slopes down to the Gault outcrop, a belt of country half a mile wide, still at this point fairly fertile, but carrying some woodland. In the middle of this belt is Boxley Abbey, situated at the confluence of two Chalk streams. The head of one of these cuts deeply into the base of the Chalk just below our footpath. The attractive village of Boxley is approached through a cherry orchard containing a row of fine walnut trees. The village street is part of the road coming down the escarpment (Boxley Hill) and crossing the Pilgrims' Way. We now follow this road south ward beside the Park which spans the whole width of the Gault belt. At its lowest point the road crosses a strike stream which joins the Medway near Sandling a mile and a half to the west. The farm and hamlet known as Harbourland are situated on the rising ground of the Folkestone Beds. Those familiar with other parts of the Vale of Holmesdale will recognize this characteristic siting, for it recurs throughout the length of the Gault–Folkestone junction line.

Penenden Heath, now a suburb of Maidstone, is a convenient finishing point of this walk. Buses run at frequent intervals from here to the centre of the town, passing the railway stations of Maidstone East (Victoria line) and Maidstone West (North Kent line). Maidstone has numerous small industries and is one of the most important centres of rural commerce in southern England. This will be evident from its shops, warehouses and waterside sites. Eight road arteries radiate from the town, leading to all parts of North Kent and the Weald and to London. The nodality of Maidstone is further emphasized by the crossing of two important railway routes and access to the town by small river craft.

7. Woldingham, Limpsfield and Oxted: the North Downs and the Holmesdale

MAPS: One-inch Ordnance Survey, Sheet 171
  1 : 25,000 Ordnance Survey, Sheets TQ(51)/35 and 45
  One-inch Geological Survey, Sheets 286 (Reigate) and 287 (Seven-oaks)

WALKING DISTANCE: 10 miles

ACCESS: Train from London Bridge or Victoria to East Croydon, thence to Woldingham, return on same line from Oxted

This excursion is essentially a N–S traverse of part of the Chalk country and the northern margin of the Weald (Fig. 30). The route is not wholly on one straight line of traverse; diversions to east and west are made in order to bring in special vantage points and local details.

A matter of interest in this particular traverse is that the crest of the North Downs and the floor of Holmesdale are here at their maximum elevation (877 feet O.D. and 475 feet O.D. respectively). From the high ground at Limpsfield the Holmesdale is graded eastward by the 'subsequent' headwaters of the river Darent which follows the strike of the Lower Greensand towards Seven-oaks, while to the west of Limpsfield the Greensand is cut up by a series of south-flowing ('obsequent') streams, tributaries of the Wealden portion of the Medway (Fig. 14).

The whole of the excursion route is shown on Sheet 171 of the one-inch map, and on the two adjacent sheets (35 and 45) of the 1 : 25,000 map. For geological detail both the Reigate and Sevenoaks sheets of the geological map are needed.

CROYDON TO WOLDINGHAM

The Croydon–Oxted railway line follows the Caterham dry valley and one of its branches as far as Woldingham. Here the line passes into a tunnel beneath the highest part of the Downs,

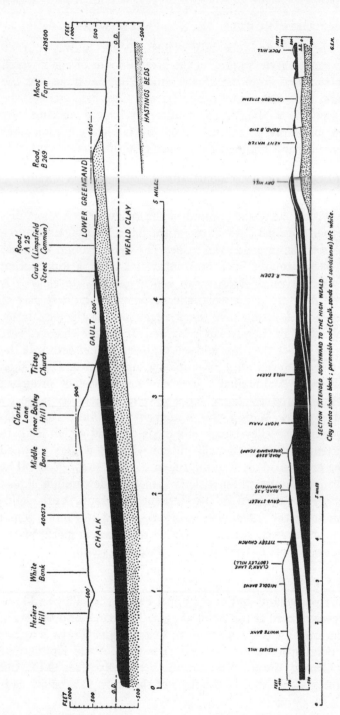

Fig. 30. Section of the northern Weald: (above) the North Downs and the Holmesdale near Limpsfield, Surrey; (below) the same extended southward over the Weald Clay outcrop to the northern flank of the High Weald near East Grinstead, Sussex

emerging at the scarp-foot NW of Oxted. The railway journey along the valleys gives an idea of the great amount of chalk which has been removed from the Downs since Pliocene times, for the valleys are both wide and deep. In the Caterham valleys the natural scenery of the Chalk country is largely obscured by suburban buildings—a striking change to those who can remember the last of the rural régime in this once beautiful countryside.

WOLDINGHAM STATION TO THE SCARP-CREST ABOVE OXTED

From Woldingham station a track runs along the east side of the railway, following the contour of the valley-side. A short distance beyond Marden Park Farm, at the point 364558, turn into a bridle road which ascends the slope. The open ground here has recently been brought back into cultivation after a long period during which typical chalk scrub vegetation had developed. A fringe of older scrub and woodland occupies the highest part of the valley-side. A little above the 700-feet contour the flat surface of a small sector of the plateau is reached. It has the characteristic covering of Clay-with-flints, and was until the second decade of the century a sequestered piece of cultivated upland around the then small village of Woldingham. It is now an outpost of suburban Surrey, dominated by fairly large modern houses in perfectly groomed gardens. Within this settlement the bridle road from the Marden Park valley becomes a made-up road which leads to the smartened relic of the old village with its houses grouped about the cross-roads and along the sides of a small green. The bridle road continues in an easterly direction, descending almost immediately into the next valley. Here the rural aspect of the landscape survives; the streamless valley floor and the more gentle slopes are cultivated, while the higher and steeper parts of the valley sides support untended chalk sward and scrub.

THE VIEW FROM THE SCARP-CREST

The footpath comes out of the upper end of the valley and joins the scarp-crest road at the point 383547. The patch of open sward above the large chalk quarries of the Oxted Lime Works is a convenient point from which to study the view of the Holmesdale and the Central Weald. The altitude here is 850 feet O.D., but as also the general level of the floor of the scarp vale below us is high (400 to 500 feet) the elevation of the Chalk crest does not appear exceptional. At the foot of the Chalk scarp there is a very distinct belt of cultivation on the Lower Chalk and Upper Greensand, contrasting with the adjacent wooded belt of the Gault outcrop which occupies the lowest ground. Beyond the Gault the Lower Greensand forms an irregular range of hills diverging from the line of the Chalk eastward, its summits rising to considerable heights in that direction (Kent Hatch 650 feet, Crockham Hill 706 feet, the Chart at Brasted, 800 feet). In the sector S of the view-point the Greensand range does not form a continuous escarpment, for it is divided by the valleys of southward-flowing (obsequent) streams. The summits between these valleys are lower in altitude (West Heath, Limpsfield, 515 feet, Beechwood Hill, 500 feet). Farther west the escarpment is again unbroken, with its crest at over 500 feet (Tilburstow Hill, S of Godstone).

One of the obsequent cuts through the Greensand range, that of the Oxted stream, runs southward over the ground immediately in front of the view-point. Its primary source of water is a series of springs rising near the base of the Chalk and distributed along some 4 miles of the scarp-foot. The Chalk streams have created a shallow semi-circular hollow in the floor of the scarp vale. They converge at Oxted to form a single stream which passes into a deep trench through the Greensand. Here, as we shall observe later, the flow is augmented by springs at the base of the Hythe Beds. The stream then flows southward over the low-lying Weald Clay to join the river Eden, a 'subsequent' tributary of the Medway.

To the west of the basin of the Oxted stream, separated from it by the high ground of the Tandridge watershed, is another large obsequent catchment containing the Godstone and Bletchingly streams which unite to form Gibbs Brook. From the view-point above Oxted this drainage basin is conspicuously marked by the profiles of its bounding watersheds.

South of the Greensand country the view embraces a wide sector of the Inner Weald, including the Weald Clay lowland some 5 miles in width and beyond it the hills of the Hastings Beds sandstones in a series of E–W ranges. The highest summits on the nearest range are Dry Hill (432417), 505 feet O.D., and Markbeech (478426), 485 feet O.D. Beyond them rises the crest of the Ashdown Forest, the main watershed of the Weald.

THE NORTH DOWNS AT TITSEY

From the view-point above Oxted quarries the simplest and most instructive route eastward is along the scarp-crest road,* for the southern slopes are here heavily wooded and belong to private estates. Beyond the shallow wind-gap (387547) at the head of the Woldingham valley the hill-top road is at a greater altitude (870 feet O.D.) than any other road on the North Downs. At intervals along it unobstructed views may be obtained down the dip-slope of the Chalk to the central parts of the London Basin. It will be observed that the high plateau of the Chalk carries a cover of Clay-with-flints. The soil, though heavy in working and very stony, is almost everywhere in arable cultivation.

At the road junction at Botley Hill (398555) follow the woodland track southward down the scarp-face to the head of Pitchfont Lane. The woodland on this slope of the downs consists almost wholly of beech, the dominant tree of most of the natural woodland on the southern Chalk; but here the woods have been artificially raised, as the name, 'Titsey Plantation', suggests. The Ordnance Map of 1819 shows that here at that date the escarpment was in the condition of open downland. The example serves to show how mature forest conforming exactly with the natural climax type can be produced in a comparatively short time by raising the species of tree appropriate to the conditions of soil and climate. There is little to distinguish this woodland at Titsey from natural woods of greater antiquity elsewhere on the downs.

* From remote times the high ridge of the North Downs has served as a line of communication between the focus of prehistoric civilization in Wiltshire and Hampshire and the coast of the Straits of Dover (p. 124-6). I. D. Margary, in recently published work (notably 'The North Downs Main Trackway and the Pilgrims' Way'—*Arch. Jour.* CIX (1953), p. 39), has shown that two distinct trackways occupy the line of the Chalk range. One of these is the 'terrace way' along the foot of the scarp, which since the advent of romantic antiquarianism has become known as the 'Pilgrims' Way'; the other is a 'ridgeway', following closely the crest of the scarp. The two tracks may have been used as alternatives according to seasonal or other conditions. In the sector of the North Downs with which we are here concerned the two trackways are typical, although as Margary points out, the 'Pilgrims' Way' or terrace way is wrongly placed on the Ordnance Maps; it should run close under Titsey Plantation, where in fact a well-defined track does exist.

THE SCARP-FOOT ZONE

Limpsfield Lodge Farm is situated at one of the springs which emerge from the Chalk at the foot of the scarp. To see the pond at the spring head and the obsequent stream to which it gives rise, turn aside from Pitchfont Lane past the farm cottages on the left. It will be seen that Titsey Park occupies a broad obsequent trench in the scarp-foot zone, its streams being tributary to the Oxted line of drainage. Beyond this hollow to the south-east the Gault and Lower Greensand country is seen to be truncated by an extensive plane at about the 500-feet O.D. level, a surface which we shall presently examine. Returning to Pitchfont Lane and following its course in the SSE direction the observer will soon be aware of his passage on to the Gault outcrop. This is indicated by the grey clay soil and the profusion of thickets and woody belts along the field boundaries, all containing numerous oaks. Cultivation on the clay lands is largely a post-war feature. Formerly the Gault surface was predominantly rough pasture land. The numerous flint pebbles and fragments seen on the surface are doubtless remnants of gravels contemporary with those which survive in the Limpsfield Common area but which have here been dispersed by the cutting of the obsequent valley. At the Titsey road (406538) the Oxted stream is crossed. Here the considerable downcutting of the stream in the Gault surface is clearly shown, and the bed of the stream is seen to contain flint and Lower Greensand rock derived from the destruction of the ancient gravel spread.

LIMPSFIELD COMMON

On entering Sandy Lane on the E side of the Titsey road the sandy Folkestone Beds are seen now to occupy the surface of the ground. The sand is revealed in the sides of the sunken lane and in the light soil of the adjacent fields. The occurrence of beech hereabouts should remind the observer of the entire absence of that species from the heavy, badly drained soils of the adjacent Gault. Above Hookwood (409534) the ground on the E side of the lane rises steeply to the edge of the gravel-covered plateau at the 500 feet altitude. A glance back to the NW provides a view of the ground traversed from the scarp-face at Oxted quarries; the belt of the Gault outcrop is clearly defined by its characteristic pastoral and wooded scenery.

At the plateau surface Sandy Lane joins the road running south-ward across Limpsfield Common. Follow this road for a short distance and then strike across the Common in a SE direction, passing through a number of overgrown shallow workings in the gravel. The gravel, composed of pebbles and fragments of flint, together with quantities of stone from the Lower Greensand rocks, forms a thin covering over the level surface of the Folkestone Beds and adjacent parts of the Gault in the neighbourhood of Grub Street. The gravel-covered area is fully $\frac{3}{4}$ square mile in extent, and is to be regarded as a relic of an ancient floor of the Holmes-dale, probably created by the ancestor of the present subsequent headwater of the Darent. The present drainage network in the area, including the Darent itself and the obsequent feeders of the Oxted stream, is cut down well below the 500-feet level, the old valley floor at this height being preserved only over a limited area of the watershed between the stream heads.

THE GREENSAND DIP-SLOPE

After crossing the central part of Limpsfield Common, follow the main road, A25, for a short distance NE of Gate House or Ballards Lane (414528) to the point where a footpath strikes south-eastward along the floor of a shallow valley. Follow the footpath in the direction of the distant spire of Chart Church. It will be noticed that the shallow valley presently turns towards ENE, and in that direction gives birth to the headwaters of the subsequent Darent, receiving at intervals obsequent tributaries from the north and consequent streams draining the Greensand upland on its south side.

The footpath runs along the southern side of a copse and joins a farm road directed southward towards Ridlands Lane. In this neighbourhood we are traversing an intensively cultivated belt, the fertility of the soil being due in part to the loamy nature of the underlying Sandgate Beds. The fertile belt extends south of Redlands Lane over ground which was formerly covered by the Sandgate Beds but which in terms of 'solid' geology is mapped as part of the Hythe Beds outcrop. Typical soil conditions of the cherty Hythe Beds still farther south are made evident by the heath vegetation in the vicinity of Little Heath and Limpsfield Chart.

DIVERSION TO LIMPSFIELD CHART

If time permits it is worth while making a diversion eastward from Little Heath to the neighbourhood of Scearn Bank in order to examine the effects of land-slipping along the Hythe Beds scarp. The upper part of the scarp-face immediately south of the Chart road is irregularly terraced and traversed by longitudinal trenches, some of them of large size with almost vertical sides. This form of the surface appears to be the result of the displacement of vertical slices of the mass of sandstone and chert as the Weald Clay beneath it has yielded under its weight. The features of the hillside cannot be viewed as a whole, as the ground is everywhere overgrown with woods and scrub, but the details are instructive and should be compared with those of the Hythe Beds scarp between Leith Hill and Coldharbour (p. 114). A great landslip in the vicinity of Crockham Hill occurred in 1596, and others have been reported at later dates.*

THE OXTED STREAM

The track from Ridlands Lane reaches the Chart road at the corner of Little Heath (421518). From this point follow a footpath westward along the boundary between the heath and Tenchley's Park. At the entrance to the park the footpath joins a wider track which begins to descend the scarp, or rather the side of a combe in the scarp-face cut by the head of an obsequent stream. The latter is parallel to the larger Oxted Stream which occupies the great obsequent gap through the Greensand range over a mile farther west. Before descending the slope the westward prospect of the Greensand hills (Fig. 31) should be studied, a convenient viewpoint for this purpose being near the head of Tenchley's Lane (416516).

The obsequent gaps of the Oxted Stream and Gibbs Brook divide the range into distinct blocks: Limpsfield, Beechwood Hill (Tandridge) and Tilburstow Hill (Godstone). Each mass in turn stands a little farther forward into the Weald, so that from this view-point Tilburstow is seen beyond the nearer profile of Beechwood Hill. The dip-slope of the latter falls away northward, and beyond it lies the scarped range of the Chalk, marked by the salients of Tandridge Hill and Gravelly Hill.

* W. Topley: *Geology of the Weald*, 1875, p. 316.

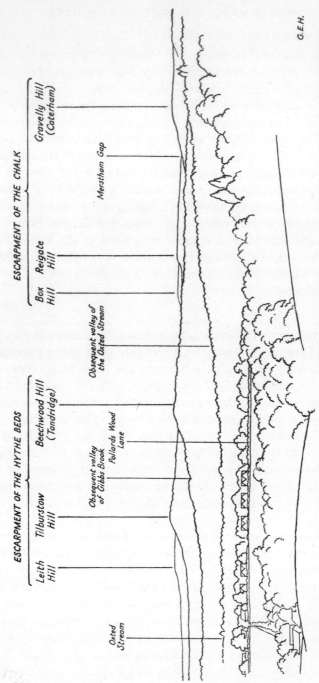

Fig. 31. Profiles of the Hythe Beds and Chalk escarpments as seen in the view westward from Tenchley's Lane, Limpsfield, Surrey

ESCARPMENT OF THE CHALK

Gravelly Hill (Caterham)

Merstham Gap

Reigate Hill

Box Hill

Obsequent valley of the Oxted Stream

ESCARPMENT OF THE HYTHE BEDS

Beechwood Hill (Tandridge)

Pollards Wood Lane

Obsequent valley of Gibbs Brook

Tilburstow Hill

Leith Hill

Oxted Stream

G.E.H.

From the view-point near Tenchley's Lane trees obstruct the view southward into the Weald, but lower down the slope there is a fine prospect of the Low Weald and the distant heights of Ashdown Forest. Towards Grants Lane water seepage near the base of the Hythe Beds becomes evident, and the Weald Clay is exposed in the bottom of the combe.

Crossing Grants Lane, enter the track beside Bolthurst Farm and follow this across the stream to Pollards Wood Lane. The footpath which formerly continued in a westerly direction no longer exists so that it is now necessary to follow a road called Pollards Oak Road through a new housing estate as far as Hurst Green Halt on the Oxted line. Here cross the railway and follow the road beside the line, turning left to pass Hurst Green Church. Continuing in the westerly direction the lane crosses the Oxted Stream at Tanhouse Farm (394513). At the Hay Cutter public house just beyond the stream a footpath strikes off to the right following the water meadows (the beginning of the alluvial flood-plain of the stream). Situated at the head of the flood-plain and the point of confluence of the main Oxted Stream and its Limpsfield tributary is the water mill of Broadham Manor. The mill is no longer used for its original purpose, but the various channels and sluices controlling the supply of water to and from the mill pond are still functioning and provide an interesting study in the harnessing of a natural stream for the purpose of providing mechanical power.

After crossing the mill-race follow the footpath NNE towards Woodhurst Park, that is along the Limpsfield branch of the stream, emerging on the road near the bridge (392522). From here it is a short walk through the newer part of Oxted to Oxted and Limpsfield station.

8. Chelsfield, Shoreham and the Darent Gap: the North Downs in Kent

MAPS: One-inch Ordnance Survey, Sheet 171
   1 : 25,000 Ordnance Survey, Sheets TQ(51)/46 and 56
   One-inch Geological Survey, Sheets 271 (Dartford) and 287 (Sevenoaks)

WALKING DISTANCE: 10 miles

ACCESS: Train from Charing Cross or London Bridge (Sevenoaks–Tonbridge line) to Chelsfield. Return from Knockholt (same line)—frequent service

This excursion is devoted to the study of the Chalk dip-slope immediately to the west of the Darent gap, and the southern part of the Darent valley itself. It has been shown (p. 12) that the dip-slope of the North Downs presents three principal facets, each associated with a recognized stage in the process of Wealden denudation. These facets are all represented in the sector of the Downs to the west of the Darent. The first is the belt of high land inclined northward from the scarp-crest at an angle of up to 2 degrees. Near the Darent gap this belt is no more than half a mile wide, but farther west, owing to the south-westerly trend of the escarpment and the increasing altitude of its crest, it becomes much wider. This highest facet of the dip-slope is to be regarded genetically as the relic, possibly modified, of an ancient Wealden land surface which was in existence before the incursion of the Pliocene sea, and remained as dry land during that episode. The surface is consistently covered by a varying thickness of Clay-with-flints.

The higher slope comes down to approximately the line of the 600-foot contour, to the north of which there is a distinct flattening of the surface. This next facet of the upland, inclined at less than 1 degree, is the wave-cut bench or platform of the Pliocene coast. The only large single area of this nearly level surface in the

158

district is between Halstead and Sepham Heath. The rest of it is a series of N–S strips separated by the dry valleys deeply incised in the Chalk. The divided surface of the Pliocene platform here does not carry deposits of sand and shingle such as those found farther west on the Downs (Headley Heath, etc.). Instead it is strewn with material derived either from Clay-with-flints or with remains of the former Eocene cover. It would appear that along this sector of the Pliocene coast the platform was cut partly in Chalk and partly in the overlying Eocene beds—at a level, that is, very near to the junction plane of the two formations.

The dry valleys which deeply score the higher parts of the Chalk mass follow a simple rectangular pattern of dissection. From the Darent gap westward to the plateau village of Downe there are nine valleys (variously branched) following more or less parallel courses down the dip-slope. The easternmost of this series of con-sequent valleys, Timberden Bottom, opens into the Darent valley just north of Shoreham. All the others are intercepted by the east or west branches of a strike valley which formerly carried the subsequent tributaries of the river Cray. It is this E–W trench which divides the high plateau of the Chalk (the Pliocene platform) from the third and lowest facet of the dip-slope, a surface from which a thick mantle of Lower Tertiary deposits has been largely removed by sub-aerial erosion since the retreat of the Pliocene sea.

It is of interest to compare the lower part of the Chalk dip-slope which lies between the Darent and the Cray with the country west of the Cray valley, for there the Tertiary cover remains intact and is essentially a plateau of the Blackheath Beds (sand and flint pebbles), with remnants of the London Clay on its higher parts. The valleys of a number of streams and their tributaries are sharply incised in the Tertiary mass, but the valleys are narrow and separated by wide stretches of unbroken plateau.

The country east of the Cray, with which we are here chiefly concerned, presents quite a different picture. A glance at the geo-logical map will show that in this sector the Tertiary cover has been so extensively breached by its former drainage network that it survives only as a number of outliers on the widely exposed Chalk. These outliers are elongated in the N–S direction. The greater part of their surface is the exposed fine sand and silt of the Thanet Beds, the lowest division of the Lower Tertiary series, the Blackheath Beds being preserved only in small patches on a number of summits corresponding roughly in altitude with the gently inclined plateau west of the Cray. It is evident, then, that in this Cray–Darent sector the Tertiary plateau has reached a more advanced stage of dissection; the country is now predominantly a Chalk tract, the Chalk itself carrying the impress of the original drainage pattern but opened out into broad valleys running tributary-wise to the main trenches of the Cray and the Darent. The valleys are now entirely streamless, like those in the high plateau beyond the head of the Cray (see p. 159). It is interesting to note that water draining from the surface of the Tertiary outliers disappears below ground by way of 'swallow holes' as soon as it reaches the highly permeable Chalk (p. 183).

An interesting and useful account of the country with which this excursion is concerned was written in 1915 by the geologist, A. L. Leach, under the title of 'Geological and Geographical Notes on Well Hill, Kent'.*

CHELSFIELD

Leave Chelsfield station by the up-platform and re-cross the railway by Warren Road, leading to Chelsfield village. The extensive arable farming here, centred on Court Lodge Farm, is typical of the Chalk lands of the lower part of the dip-slope. That the soil is derived directly from the Chalk is made evident by the abundance of *calcicolous* shrubs and herbs in the hedgerows. Continue eastward across the Orpington By-pass to the small nucleus of Chelsfield village, which is situated on a small outlier of Lower Tertiaries including a capping of the pebbly Blackheath Beds. It is interesting to note that numerous prehistoric flint artefacts have been found on this outlier. Chelsfield is typical of the Chalk upland villages in that it consists of numerous widely scattered hamlets and farms, the nucleus itself being of only small size. The original parish was large; it is now incorporated with several other rural parishes in the comparatively new urban unit of Orpington in the Cray valley.

CHELSFIELD TO WELL HILL

From Chelsfield follow the road eastward towards Shoreham

* *Proc. Geol. Assoc.* XXVI (1915), p. 342.

(Bucks Cross Road and Hawstead Lane), observing the large size of the farms in this neighbourhood. There are good views in the direction NNW across the Cray valley, some 3 miles distant, to Shooters Hill in the Thames valley.

Hawstead Lane is directed towards the western flank of the large Well Hill Tertiary outlier, which is seen as a ridge some 3 miles in length from N to S, the highest part of its crest being about 150 feet above the general level of the Chalk surface on which it rests. It is distinguished not only by its height and the steepness of its slopes but by the dense tree cover which causes it to stand out in marked contrast to the relatively treeless Chalk country around it. The woods are mainly on the southern half of the mass, but over the northern part continuous orchard land takes the place of woodland.

Geologically the Well Hill outlier consists of a thick mass of Thanet Sand overlain by Woolwich Beds (mainly clay) which occupy a narrow strip of ground along the crest of the ridge. This is surmounted on the highest ground by patches of coarse gravel, but it is remarkable that there are no Blackheath Beds on the outlier. The continuation of Hawstead Lane ascends Well Hill as a deeply sunken lane with the yellow Thanet Sand exposed in the banks. After seeing this exposure return to the corner (494639) to follow the lane which branches NNE along the contour of the hillside, as here may be seen one of the small streams which flow from the Tertiary cover only to disappear underground a little farther down the slope.

The lane turns sharply eastward at the public house ('The Kent Hounds') and in a very short distance joins the road running along the crest of the Well Hill Ridge. It is necessary to follow this road southward for ¾ mile and return again if the hill-top gravels are to be examined and discussed. Whether or not this diversion is undertaken, a view-point on the ridge road (c. 498641) should be sought in order to study the distant parts of the country over the wide arc from NW to SE. On a clear day the view over London from Well Hill is one of the finest that can be had. It shows the great expanse of London's built-up area between and around the highest hills of the lower Thames valley, Shooters Hill and Crystal Palace on the south and the northern heights around Hampstead and Highgate beyond. Industrial Thames-side is seen stretching eastward beyond Dartford, which lies NE of the view-point. There is an excellent prospect of the Darent gap, and the view eastward across it shows the North Downs in an impressive profile from the scarp above Otford, across the high plateau and down to the lower parts of the dip-slope at Horton Kirby. Nearer at hand we have a good picture of the agricultural development of the Chalk lands and the Tertiary outliers. The light soils of the Thanet Sands over the northern parts of the Well Hill outlier are marked by the concentration of orchards and bush fruit plantations, with some fields cultivated for potatoes and other market garden crops. On the higher parts of the ridge about us there has grown up a colony of smallholders whose husbandry depends on the fertility and easy working of the sandy soil. The Chalk areas beyond the outlier between NW and E are seen to be in extensive arable cultivation. The fields are large and woodlands and woody hedgerows reduced to a minimum. This is in contrast not only with the land on the Tertiary outlier but also with that in the dry valley running eastward to the main trench of the Darent. This valley is occupied almost entirely with the woods and pastures of Lullingstone Park, part of which is presently to be traversed.

DIVERSION TO THE SUMMIT OF WELL HILL

The road along the crest of the Well Hill ridge runs southward past a reservoir (496637) and between cottages and smallholdings to the high ground of Hollows (Hollards) Wood at an altitude of 600 feet O.D. At this altitude there are patches of coarse gravel resting on clays and loams of the Woolwich Beds (c. 497632). The gravel areas may be readily identified by the change in the vegetation from coppiced oakwood to woods of the oak-birch-heath type. The gravel is not exposed anywhere in section but there are occasional bare patches where it is possible to examine the deposit. It will be seen to contain large, battered flints, angular and sub-angular flint fragments, white or deep-brown in colour, and many flint pebbles like those found in the Blackheath Beds. There are also small quartz pebbles and rolled and angular pieces of Lower Greensand chert. All these materials lie in a matrix of coarse red sand.

The question of the origin of the Well Hill gravel occasioned much speculation on the part of early geologists. The proximity

4 The view across the Darent gap from the downs above Shoreham

of the deposit to the Darent gap tempted some writers to associate it with the early history of that valley. We should not now, however, hesitate to assign the gravel to the period of the Pliocene marine transgression, for its position on a summit at 600 feet O.D., and its unmistakable contents, proclaim its kinship with similar deposits similarly situated on the uplands north of the Weald. It is of interest to note in the light of what has been said above (p. 159) that here farther to the north (owing to the northerly dip of the strata) the offshore platform of the Pliocene littoral was cut in a substantial thickness of Eocene material. It is interesting, too, that the occurrence of Pliocene gravel on the Eocene outlier at Well Hill is paralleled at Headley in Surrey, where similar gravel (a mere trace in that instance) lies on the 600-foot summit of Nower Wood (p. 78). The parallel goes further in that the outliers of Nower Wood and Well Hill stand in a rather similar relationship to the pattern of post-Pliocene dissection of the surrounding Chalk.

The southward continuation of the track through Hollows Wood is no longer public. It leads to the road between Chelsfield and Shoreham, an interesting and attractive route into the Darent valley by way of Timberden Bottom. The alternative—returning northward along the ridge of Well Hill—has much to commend it, and is the route now to be described.

WELL HILL TO LULLINGSTONE PARK

From the vicinity of the 'Kent Hounds' (497643), or the viewpoint (c. 498641), follow the road northward for a short distance downhill, turn sharply to the right into the lane leading to Great Cockerhurst, and then left by a farm at the roadside. Field tracks for ½ mile lead to Parkgate (506646), the western entrance to Lullingstone Park. After entering the park take the footpath in the SE direction, crossing a stretch of grassland and leading into the woods which clothe the sides of the Lullingstone valley. The woods on the south side are composed of beech, oak and hornbeam. They are of considerable age, woodland probably having survived here from the remote past while all the rest of the Chalk upland has been brought entirely into arable cultivation.

It may be mentioned that an excursion to Well Hill and on to Lullingstone Park could be made the occasion of a visit to the

12

recently excavated Roman villa at Lullingstone (530650). This
ranks as one of the most important Roman domestic sites in the
country, revealing evidence of occupation from the first to the
fourth centuries A.D. and of the existence of Romano-British
Christianity. The Lullingstone discovery is fully described in a
book by its principal investigator.*

The walk through the park to the Roman site and then by one or
other of the routes to Shoreham would add about 3 miles to the
day's walk. Also inspection of the site would occupy some time.
Therefore the visit could hardly be regarded as a possible addition
to the Chelsfield–Shoreham route as described, and readers intend-
ing to go to Lullingstone might do well to make their return to
London from Eynsford station.

LULLINGSTONE PARK TO SHOREHAM

The footpath crossing the head of the valley in Lullingstone
Park comes out on to a cultivated plateau and leads to a point
(511637) on the lane running E–W through the large farm called
Great Cockerhurst. On the opposite side of the lane, a very short
distance E, another footpath continues the southerly route. At
the second of two derelict bungalows (512635) the track strikes
almost due S along a field boundary towards Coombe Hollow.

One noticeable point about the stretch of cultivated upland
between Cockerhurst and Coombe Hollow is its very stony soil.
The geological map indicates here a spread of Clay-with-flints,
but the covering is not the true Clay-with-flints of the higher parts
of the Chalk to the south of us. The Geological Survey Memoir
on the Dartford Sheet does indeed qualify the generalization
adopted on the published map by referring to the superficial deposit here as the 'Brown Flint Drift' of earlier geological writers.
It consists mainly of flints, many of them stained dark brown,
Tertiary pebbles, and a small number of fragments of Lower
Greensand material (ragstone, chert and ironstone). The deposit
is remarkable for the frequent occurrence in it of brown flint
casts of Chalk fossils, especially echinoderms; but of greater interest and significance is the occurrence in the deposit of human
artefacts, chiefly flint palaeoliths of the 'ovate' form. This is
evidence enough that we have here a deposit of post-Pliocene age;

* G. W. Meates: *Lullingstone Roman Villa*. London, 1955. Heinemann.

and its position on a gently inclined flat within the trough of the Darent, though high above the present river (over 400 feet O.D.), suggests that it is a relic of an older floor of the valley. The serial sections in Fig. 32 give point to this suggestion.

From the point 513631, at the lip of Coombe Hollow, there is a good view of the entrance of the Darent gap and of the high range of the Greensand to the south. Immediately below the view-point is the branched dry valley of Timberden Bottom opening into the side of the main Darent valley. It shows well the valley-bottom cultivation contrasting with the woodland cover of the slopes, a characteristic of so many North Down valleys. From here, too, the reader may look back across the upland flat to Great Cocker-hurst, and towards the wooded flank of Well Hill which stands like a wall against the western margin of the bench. In this view of a large stretch of country nearly at eye-level one gets the impression that there are here two distinct erosion surfaces at slightly different levels, one at 425–450 feet O.D., the other at 475–500 feet.

The footpath now turns SE to join the lane along Coombe Hollow, which continues downhill and across the floor of Timber-den Bottom. The reader may now choose between a direct ascent to the crest of the acute ridge of Meenfold Hill standing between Timberden Bottom and the Darent, and a short diversion to Shoreham, ascending the steep eastern slope of the ridge after looking at the village. Unlike many valley villages Shoreham has no expanse of terrace on which to spread. It occupies a site in the valley where the flood-plain is narrow, one of its streets crossing the valley floor and containing the bridge, another at right angles to it running for half a mile along the contour of the valley side. Shoreham contains buildings of widely ranging age in various styles of Kentish rural architecture. Many locally derived building materials are to be seen here, such as flint, brick, tiles, ragstone, timber and thatch.

SHOREHAM TO HALSTEAD AND KNOCKHOLT STATION

Follow the southward road (along the 200-foot contour) through and beyond the village to a point (c. 515610) where a signposted public footpath strikes off at right angles and ascends the valley side. Near the summit of Meenfold ridge (510612) the view back across the Darent gap is one of the loveliest in southern England.

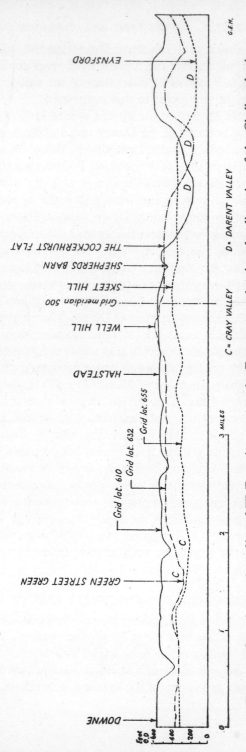

Fig. 32. Superimposed profiles of W-E sections across the Darent gap, showing the dissection of the Chalk upland

DOWNE

GREEN STREET GREEN

HALSTEAD

WELL HILL

SKEET HILL

SHEPHERDS BARN

THE COCKERHURST FLAT

EYNSFORD

Grid lat. 610

Grid lat. 632

Grid lat. 655

Grid meridian 500

C = CRAY VALLEY   D = DARENT VALLEY

C

D

Feet
O.D.
600
400
200
0

0   1   2   3 MILES

G.E.M.

From the view-point the footpath continues to Shepherd's Barn in the head of the Timberden valley, from whence a farm track leads westward to the London–Sevenoaks road, A21. At this point (500609) we are on the Pliocene bench of the Downs and will continue so through the village of Halstead until the surface breaks into the slopes of the great E–W valley which divides the Chalk dip-slope. Various tracks and footpaths lead from the main road A21 to Halstead. The almost level ground is seen to have soil derived from Clay-with-flints, or from the Lower Tertiary beds. It is intensively cultivated for vegetables and fruit. On the North Downs generally it is exceptional for cultivation of this type to extend as far south on to the high plateau.

From Halstead village (488611) take the road leading NW and follow it as far as the Rectory. Here a footpath strikes due N and runs for ¾ mile across the flat upland fields and orchards. It then descends through a strip of parkland to the Sevenoaks road in the bottom of the dry valley, at a point less than 200 yards from Knockholt station.

9. Lingfield, Dry Hill and Kent Water: a Study of the High Weald

MAPS: One-inch Ordnance Survey, Sheet 171
　　1 : 25,000 Ordnance Survey, Sheets TQ(51)/34, 43 and 44. Only a very small part of the end of the route comes on Sheet 43 of this series
　　One-inch Geological Survey, Sheet 287 (Sevenoaks). This map gives only part of the route—Lingfield to Dry Hill, but it presents the broad picture of the geology of the northern flank of the Weald and is therefore useful in the interpretation of the northerly views. For this purpose it would even be useful to carry Sheet 286 (Reigate) as well
　　Bartholomew's Half-inch Map, Sheet 6 (Sussex). This is the best map for showing broadly the topography of the Central Weald, and a most useful aid to the identification of distant features and places seen from the high view-points

WALKING DISTANCE: 7 miles

ACCESS: Train from London Bridge or Victoria via East Croydon (Tunbridge Wells line) to Lingfield. Return from East Grinstead (same line). Green Line Coach, Service 708 (Hemel Hempstead, London, Croydon and East Grinstead) to Lingfield. Return from East Grinstead

---

The country traversed on this excursion is the part of the High Weald which lies nearest to London. It is selected for our purpose partly because of its accessibility, being near the routes of the public transport services between London and East Grinstead. The piece of country to be traversed is no more than a small fragment of the great Central Wealden upland, yet it displays many of the characteristic features of that terrain, and includes one of its best, yet least known view-points. This is Dry Hill (430417), very near the point where the county boundaries of Kent, Surrey and Sussex meet, and a place which is strangely remote from any village or main road.

The High Weald, as we have shown (p. 23), is the upstanding mass of sandstones and clays (the Hastings Beds) laid bare by the stripping back of its former covering of Weald Clay and higher strata. The Weald Clay now lies against the flanks of the central mass, reduced to a broad lowland between it and the scarped ridges of the Wealden margins. The initial denudation of the Central Weald, destined later to expose a large area of the Hastings Beds, was begun well back in Tertiary times. By late Miocene or early Pliocene times an extensive peneplain had been produced, and along some of the anticlinal axes at any rate, this surface must have been cut below the base of the Weald Clay. The further exposure of the Hastings Beds and the sculpturing of the ridges and valleys of the High Weald to the form in which we now know them has been the work of rivers during and since Pliocene times.

Stratigraphically the Hastings Beds are constituted of alternating sandstones and clays, the former predominating. The clay beds vary in thickness from a foot or two upwards, and only one clay unit, the Wadhurst Clay, reaches any great thickness (as much as 140 feet near East Grinstead). This layer is indeed one of the principal subdivisions of the Hastings Beds, sandwiched between a sandstone series above (the Tunbridge Wells Sand) and another below (the Ashdown Sand), each with its own subdivisions, including minor clay strata.

As regards structure, the Hastings Beds present an intricate complex of folds and faults, the general trend of which is east–west. The general anticlinal form of the Weald as a whole is legible in the High Weald to the extent that the Ashdown Sand, the lowest division of the Hastings Beds, has its main outcrop over the highest ground near the centre of the mass, whilst the Tunbridge Wells Sand, the uppermost division, is more in evidence along the flanks. But there is otherwise nothing in the disposition of the outcrops to suggest a *simple* anticlinal fold. The geological map indeed shows that the Hastings Beds have been greatly puckered and disrupted, a condition which is evident enough to any who attempt to investigate in the field the anatomy of any Central Wealden landscape.

There is plenty of evidence that the drainage and dissection of the High Weald has been fairly closely controlled by its constituent folds.* The central watershed dividing the Medway on the north from the Ouse on the south itself follows approximately the axis of the Ashdown Forest anticline. The headward end of the Medway, flowing eastward through Forest Row and Hartfield, occupies part of the complementary synclinal trough. Its tributary, the Kent Water, follows a nearly parallel course along the next syncline, while the Eden, the largest subsequent feeder of the Medway, flowing on the Weald Clay, approximates to the line of yet another structural trough. The minor tributaries in this system are also predominantly strike streams, their northerly links being generally short. The East Grinstead sector of the High Weald is thus seen to be broadly a series of east–west ridges and valleys sculptured by streams initiated at higher levels, but in courses directly determined by the Mid-Tertiary folding of the Wealden rocks.

Lingfield lies at the foot of the northern slopes of the Hastings Beds, and the walking route from the village takes us at first eastward along the lower ground, then southward over the first of the prominent ridges—over the summit of Dry Hill—and down into the valley of the Kent Water. The latter is of particular interest from its association with the Wealden iron industry of

* For a discussion of this subject see *Structure, Surface and Drainage in South East England*, chapter viii, p. 76.

former days. The walk ends at Holtye on the next ridge to the south, which gives convenient access to East Grinstead by road.

LINGFIELD

The nucleus of the village of Lingfield stands on a level platform of Tunbridge Wells Sand at about 225 feet O.D. Surfaces at approximately the same height are widely distributed over the adjacent lowland of the Weald Clay, the river Eden and its numerous affluents having created broad valley floors some 80 feet below the plane of these now separated plateaux.

The fertility of the soil on Lingfield's small platform is evident from the orchard land hereabouts, particularly on the south-facing slope which forms one side of the valley of the Eden Brook. The older part of the village is clustered around a loose convergence of country roads, which suggests the early importance of Lingfield as the focus of a rural territory. A point of considerable interest here, as in most Wealden villages and towns, is the use of a wide variety of locally derived building materials. These include sandstone, bricks, tiles, stone roofing slabs (Horsham Stone) and much timber. The wealth of building materials in the Weald has induced a high standard of rural craftsmanship only surpassed by that of one or two other favoured regions in the country. The village church of Lingfield and its contents are of considerable historic interest.

LINGFIELD TO DRY HILL

Leave the village by the road, B2028, running eastward across the valley of the Eden Brook. Continue on this road to Dormans Corner and beyond Beechurst to a point (409428) near Woodgate, where a drive directed ESE leads into the extensive park of Ford Manor. Near a lodge cottage a small tributary of the Eden Brook is crossed and the drive becomes a sunken way with the Upper Tunbridge Wells Sand exposed in its banks. Farther along the drive there are views northward across the Low Weald to the escarpment of the Lower Greensand.

Continue in the ESE direction, crossing the main drive to Ford Manor at the point 416425. At the crossing of the next stream pass through a gate, turn sharp left and then right. The track then follows an easterly direction past stable buildings and a cottage,

beyond which it becomes a bridle way. A locked gate stands across
it but this is by-passed by a small footway. The track now runs
alongside a stream channel cut deeply into a stratum of clay. This
is the Grinstead Clay marking the convenient division between
Upper and Lower Tunbridge Wells Sand. Beyond Littleworth
Cottage (424426) the bridle way continues to Hoopers Farm, but
near the cottage a track strikes off to the right (ESE), leading
ultimately to Dry Hill House. The track follows a field boundary
against the north side of a high hedge. Across the open country to
the NE the escarpment of the Hythe Beds again comes into view.
The high ridges of Tilburstow Hill, Limpsfield Chart, Crockham
Hill, Ide Hill and River Hill can be identified.

At the eastern side of the cultivated field the track passes through
a gate into a wood. At this point we leave the Upper Tunbridge
Wells Sand and pass once more on to the narrow outcrop of the
Grinstead Clay. This is indicated by the soil and the vegetation
of the wood (coppice-with-standards), which contains a number of
species characteristic of moist situations. The woodland track
crosses the head of a small valley where a spring gives rise to a
small north-flowing affluent of the Eden. Reference to the geological section (Fig. 33) showing the northerly dip of the Tunbridge Wells sand in this vicinity will explain the emergence of
water at the junction of the *lower* sandstone and the overlying
Grinstead Clay.

Near the spring there is a derelict pump house. Just beyond
this small building turn right at a crossing of the woodland tracks
to follow the one which leads south towards Dry Hill House.
This track divides, one branch leading into a field. Keep to the
branch which remains for some distance within the wood (Rey-
nolds Wood) and emerges on open grassland higher up the hill.
At the farm marked Dry Hill House (429420) the bridle road to
the summit of Dry Hill goes first through an entrance by a large
oak into a farmyard and passes on the east side of the house.

DRY HILL

The best point from which to study the northerly view from Dry
Hill is at the edge of the belt of trees near the summit (430418).
In direction the view extends from a little south of west well
round into the northerly sector, thus embracing some 30 miles of

the northern scarpland belt of the Weald, dominated by the crests
of the Chalk and the Lower Greensand ranges. Along the North
Downs it is possible to identify the Mole gap, Box Hill, Betchworth Clump, Reigate Hill, Gravelly Hill, the Godstone gap,
Oxted Quarries and Botley Hill. The view due W shows the
Leith Hill upland standing forward into the Weald far south of
the line of the Chalk scarp. This aspect of the hills reproduces
perfectly the profile shown in the transect, Fig. 26.* Other parts
of the Greensand range which stand out prominently are Redhill,
Tilburstow Hill, the high ground south of Limpsfield and the
still higher summit of Crockham Hill. From our present view-
point the easterly continuation of the range through Toys Hill,
Ide Hill and River Hill near Sevenoaks is hidden by trees, though
it could have been seen from various points in the neighbourhood
of Dry Hill House.

So far we have considered only the hill features in the more distant parts of the view. Between these ranges and the High Weald
on which we stand lies the broad lowland of the Weald Clay, the
Low Weald as it is aptly called. The portion of this tract which
spreads out before us is fully 8 miles wide in the neighbourhood
of the Mole, but immediately north of our view-point, in the
direction of Limpsfield Chart, it is less than half that width (see
Fig. 33). In this lowland we may identify the small towns of Horley
to the west and Edenbridge to the NNE, as well as a number of its
widely scattered villages.

Apart from the magnificent views it affords, the summit of Dry
Hill is of great interest as a large fortified hilltop site probably of
the Early Iron Age. An area of about 27 acres over the highest
part of the hill is surrounded by a double ditch and banks, the
outline being rounded on the northern side but rectangular
between SW and SE. The earthworks are very well preserved
south-eastward from the point where the track from Dry Hill
House enters the enclosure. Little is known of the pre-Roman
people who inhabited the High Weald, but it is possible that their
tribal territories consisted of blocks of upland between the larger
valleys and that a commanding summit like Dry Hill was selected
in each for the establishment of a central fortified township.

* Fig. 26 represents the cross-section as if viewed from the west, so for
comparison with the view from Dry Hill the diagram should be reversed.

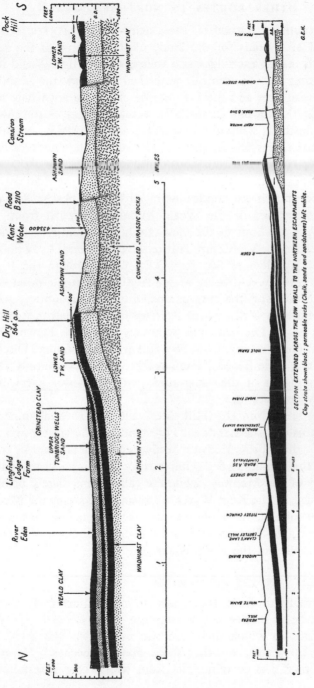

Fig. 33. Section across part of the northern flank of the High Weald: (above) the Dry Hill area, showing folding and faulting of the Hastings Beds; (below) the same section extended to the North Downs

The southern corner of the earthwork (433415) affords an excellent view-point for the study of the country to the south, that is the east–west ridges and valleys of the High Weald itself, culminating in the central watershed through the Ashdown Forest, with here and there a glimpse of the distant Chalk range of the South Downs. To the SW, 3 miles distant, is the town of East Grinstead, with its conspicuous church tower, occupying one of the ridges within the western end of the Medway basin. Beyond it is the crest of the watershed on which stand the water tower of Selsfield Common and the village of West Hoathly, with its spired church. In conditions of all but the best visibility the central watershed of the Weald, running eastward from West Hoathly, is the limit of the view. Its highest summits are Wych Cross (*c.* S 10° W), Camp Hill (*c.* S 15° E) and Crowborough (*c.* S 35° E), all over 600 feet O.D., Crowborough the highest summit in the Weald being at 792 feet. Still farther round to the east (*c.* S 60° E) is the curious domed hill of Saxonbury, 4 miles S of Tunbridge Wells, which like Dry Hill has an Iron Age foȓti-fied site on it. The principal points on the South Downs which are occasionally visible from Dry Hill are Wolstonbury, Ditchling Beacon and Firle Beacon. High as these are, they are only visible by the accident of their alignment with the lower parts of the central watershed.

In the view from Dry Hill three valleys in E–W alignment lie between us and the Ashdown Forest ridge. The largest and most distant is that of the Medway headwater; the small middle trench beyond the Hammerwood–Holtye ridge contains a nearly parallel tributary of the Medway; while the valley immediately below us is occupied by the Kent Water, a stream which joins the Medway after the turn of the latter into its northerly course towards the Penshurst gap. We now descend the southern slope of Dry Hill into the valley of the Kent Water.

THE VALLEY OF THE KENT WATER

The footpath from the south view-point descends the hill through fields to Beeches Farm. The slope is partly on Wad-hurst Clay, in which there are two overgrown clay pits, both holding up water, on the slope above Beeches. These are derelict marl pits or mine pits from which clay ironstone was obtained when iron manufacture was a flourishing industry in the Weald.

Iron working in the Weald may have begun in Iron Age times. It was certainly practised to a limited extent during the Roman occupation of Britain, and became a widespread industry during the Middle Ages. The blast furnace for manufacturing cast iron was introduced at the end of the fifteenth century and casting was used chiefly for making cannon. From this time also the process of manufacturing wrought iron was improved, and by the eighteenth century the Weald had what was for that period a vast iron industry. With the invention of coke and its use in the blast furnace iron manufacture shifted to the neighbourhood of the great coalfields and the Wealden industry declined rapidly. The last furnace (at Ashburnham) was closed in 1810. Wealden iron manufacture depended on three principal factors: iron ore, chiefly clay ironstone, which was abundant and of good quality in the Wealden rocks; fuel, in the form of charcoal, plentiful at first from the forests of the region but later obtained only at the expense of great devastation of the woodlands; and lastly power for operating bellows, hammers and other machinery—supplied by streams and rivers through the medium of water wheels. The valley of the Kent Water contained two famous iron works (blast furnaces), while at Beeches there was a bloomery for manufacturing wrought iron.*

The footpath at Beeches has been diverted to the west side of the farm, where it passes through a gate near some outlying buildings and joins the farm road leading down to the valley bottom via Hawksnest Wood. This road has been made up with material imported from a distance. It contains quantities of dark brown ironstone which might be taken for the local iron ore; it is in fact carstone from the Folkestone Beds.

On reaching the valley road turn east towards Basing Farm where, at a road fork (438402), the fine-grained sandstone of the Ashdown Sand may be seen exposed in the bank. The fine Wealden building of Basing farmhouse shows a typical combination of building materials—brick, wall tiles, timber and stone roofing

* For the history and detailed survey of Wealden iron working the reader should consult the following works: Ernest Straker: *Wealden Iron*. Bell, 1931. G. S. Sweeting: 'Wealden Iron Ore and the History of its Industry', *Proc. Geologists' Assoc.* vol. 55 (1944), p. 1.

slabs. The farm is situated at what was once the head of the great millpond of the Scarlets ironworks 500 yards farther downstream. Quite a half of this pond has become silted up and invaded by vegetation. Near Basing Farm may be seen areas of reed swamp with maturing alder-willow scrub invading it from the valley sides.

The site of the ironworks at Scarlets (formerly Scalehurst) (443401) is occupied by the flour mill which succeeded it, but which is also now disused (the mill wheel was recently dismantled). The principle of harnessing the stream for driving a wheel by building a dam across the valley to create a fall is easily understood from a glance at this example. The roadway over the dam (a private road belonging to the house at Scarlets) is paved with quantities of blast furnace slag and iron cinder. The slag is glass-like, and dark green in colour. The house and cottage at Scarlets are the sixteenth-century buildings associated with the iron works here, which was famous for nearly 200 years for the quality of its product.

Continue along the valley road to the point where it forks (448400), a place appropriately named Pondtail. This is the upstream end of another large mill pond (Furnace Pond), which was the source of water power for the Lower Furnace at Cowden. East of the road-fork a low cliff of sandstone (Ashdown Sand) runs for some distance along the valley-side, with the road and the margin of the pond at its foot. About 20 yards from the road-fork there is a small cave at the bottom of the cliff. This is thought to be the entrance to a shaft which gave access to a lower stratum of stone used for furnace building. The shaft is now filled in.

Furnace Pond, like that of Scarlets, is gradually silting up, although a large area of open water remains. At the upper end a dense thicket of alder, willow and birch occupies the marginal zone, while extensive colonies of reeds encroach upon the open water. A good view of the pond and its wooded surroundings may be obtained from the end of the dam (455400). The valley road occupies the top of the dam, and as we pass over it the house of Furnace Mill is seen on the low-level side.

THE HOLTYE RIDGE

After crossing the dam of Furnace Pond leave the road and enter a track which runs along a small tributary valley. Turn left to ascend one of the numerous paths through the bracken on the slopes of Holtye Common. The higher parts of the Common are used as a golf course. We may notice here that the vegetation is a variety of the heath community. Heather and ling are locally abundant, while bracken dominates considerable areas. The woody growth nearer the margins has the composition of the oak-birch-heath association. In the Central Weald the Ashdown Sands more often produce podsolic soils than do the Tunbridge Wells Sands. Over the latter, due perhaps to a greater admixture of clay, there are often accumulations of loam which hold moisture and restrict percolation. There is therefore more cultivation and more damp oakwood on the Tunbridge Wells Sand areas. In contrast the Ashdown Sand outcrops, as this example shows, are to a great extent characterized by dry oakwood, heathland and heathy pastures.

Cross the golf course in the SE direction to the road junction at the White Horse Inn. This is a convenient point from which to travel to East Grinstead by bus. Buses stop here at 10 minutes before and 20 minutes after the even hours. There may thus be an interval in which to consider a further subject of interest in the neighbourhood—a portion of the trans-Wealden Roman road from London to Lewes.

From the White Horse follow the Tunbridge Wells road for a short distance eastward. This road, it may be noted, is typical of the roads in the High Weald in that it keeps to the crests of the ridges, descending to valley bottoms only at necessary crossing points. The southward prospect from the ridge road shows again the dominant E–W dissection of the Hastings Beds upland and the gentle irregularities in the profile of the central watershed, particularly the dry gap at Nutley between the high summits at Camp Hill and Wych Cross.

At the point 462392 a track leads southward from the road to an exposed portion of the pavement of the Roman road. A notice at the head of the track explains briefly the significance of the site and the circumstances of its investigation. I. D. Margary has described in detail this Roman way from London, across the North Downs at Tatsfield, through Limpsfield, Edenbridge and the Ashdown Forest to the South Downs near Lewes. In his admirable book * Margary mentions the proximity of the road to

* I. D. Margary: *Roman Ways in the Weald*. 1948. London, Phoenix House.

various iron-working sites, and the use of slag as road metal for its surface. The excavated portion of the road surface which is on view in the field shows the remains of such paving, but since its excavation some years ago it had been greatly disintegrated by frost and rain. It was first revealed by the removal of a foot or more of accumulated soil, and was at that time a ribbon of iron slag, over 15 feet wide, 12 inches thick at the centre, 3 inches at the edges, the material having rusted into a hard mass. The surface was smooth and hard, but showed distinct wheel-ruts.

V The Country North of London

··

10. The Mimms Valley: the Northern Margin of the Tertiary Country

MAPS: One-inch Ordnance Survey New Popular Sheet 160
   1 : 25,000 Ordnance Survey Map, Sheet 52/20 (which contains the whole of the route)
   One-inch Geological Survey (New Series, 'Drift' edition), Sheet 239 (Hertford). Sufficient geological detail of the ground to be covered is given in the map on p. 181 (Fig. 34)
   In addition, the One-inch Geological Survey (North East London Sheet) will be useful for the study of some of the distant views

WALKING DISTANCE: (if returning from South Mimms) 7 miles; (if returning from Brookman's Park) 5½ miles

ACCESS TO SOUTH MIMMS: Bus service 84 from Arnos Grove station via High Barnet Bus service 313 from Enfield via Potters Bar
   Bus service 29 from Wood Green via Southgate and Potters Bar
   Green Line Coach service 727 (King's Cross to Luton via Highgate, North Finchley and Barnet)—half-hourly service
   If it is intended to return from Brookman's Park by train, the outward journey may also be made by train from King's Cross, Finsbury Park, etc. to Potters Bar. South Mimms may then be reached by bus from Potters Bar (services 29 and 313)

GENERAL ACCOUNT OF THE AREA ON SHEET 52/20 OF THE
   1 : 25,000 SERIES

The country shown on Sheet 52/20 of the 1 : 25,000 map lies on the margin of the Tertiary outcrop of the London Basin and presents, in typical association, many of the features of structure and surface which recur in the London countrysides. It also well illustrates the characteristic settlement pattern and land used of the much larger region of which it is part. Features of special interest in the area are the swallow holes near North Mimms

13   179

which, under normal conditions of weather, carry underground the waters of a headstream of the River Colne.

Study of the map shows that the highest ground, just exceeding 400 feet, lies in the south-west corner of the sheet around Ridge and Ridgehill, and from Potters Bar northwards to Epping Green on its eastern side. Below the general plateau level represented by these summits the valleys of the district are carved. The high ground in the east of the area throws off drainage northward and eastward to the River Lea, but the main stream of the area is Mimmshall Brook which enters our area near the point 232200 and flows northward for three miles to Water End. Beyond the swallow holes here, surface flow is only maintained after exceptionally wet weather, but the line of the valley can be traced northwestward to Colney Heath, and it carries surface drainage for a mile or more south of the village.

STRUCTURE AND RELIEF

In broad terms the geological structure of the area is exceedingly simple, the Chalk with the overlying Eocene beds dipping gently southward towards London. There are, however, local complications in the structure which affect the outcrops of the Chalk and the Reading Beds. London Clay underlies the greater part of the area, but the Reading Beds and Chalk crop out from beneath it not only along the edge of the main clay outcrop from Ridgehill to Hatfield and Essendon, but on the flanks and floor of the Mimms valley and its chief tributaries. The Reading Beds are seen also in valley inliers north of Northaw and the Chalk itself is close to the surface along the northern edge of Great Wood Northaw (c. 297043), where it is seen in swallow holes.

The appearance of the Chalk around South Mimms, well within the main Tertiary outcrop, itself suggests the influence of minor local folding bringing it nearer the surface. In Fig. 34 the level above Ordnance Datum of the top of the Chalk (where it is in contact with the overlying Reading Beds) is indicated at ten points where wells have been sunk. This evidence, taken with the varying elevation of the Chalk–Reading Beds junction along its outcrop, enables us to draw sub-surface contours for the top of the Chalk. These are shown in Fig. 34 and clearly define an anticline trending a little north of east from Ridgehill to the eastern margin

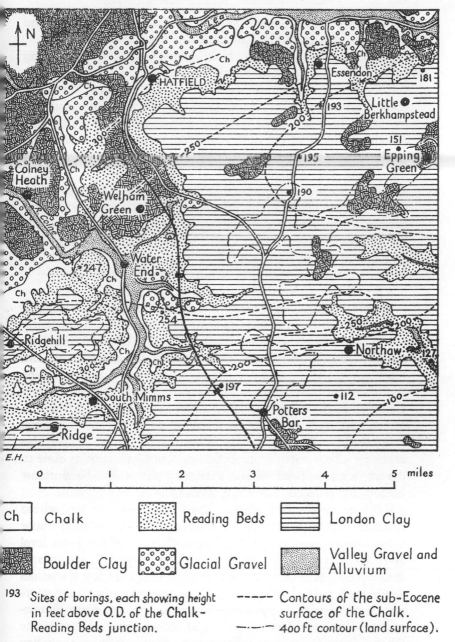

Key labels within the map:

N

Lea

Ch
HATFIELD
Essendon
Ch
181

193
200
Little
Berkhampstead

Ch
Ch
250
195
151
Epping
Green

300
190

Colney
Heath
Ch
Welham
Green
Colne

247
Water
End
Ch
Ch
254

250
200
Ridgehill
Ch
Northaw
127
Ch
300
Ch
200
197
112
100
South Mimms
Potters
Bar

Ridge

E.H.

| 0 | 1 | 2 | 3 | 4 | 5 miles |

| Ch | Chalk | | Reading Beds | | London Clay |

Boulder Clay   Glacial Gravel   Valley Gravel and Alluvium

193   Sites of borings, each showing height in feet above O.D. of the Chalk-Reading Beds junction.

-----   Contours of the sub-Eocene surface of the Chalk.

—·—·—   400 ft contour (land surface).

Fig. 34.   Geological map of the country around the Mimms valley, Hertfordshire

of our area. Along this axis the top of the Chalk is for the most part above 250 feet O.D. and between North and South Mimms it exceeds 300 feet, standing higher than in any other part of the area. Southward from the axis the beds decline gently towards the south or south-east; beneath Barvin Park (237010), the Chalk must lie at about 100 feet O.D., implying a southerly dip of between 1 and 2 degrees from the axis of the anticline north of Northaw. North of the anticlinal axis the rocks are bent into a gentle syncline, the centre of the trough running from North Mimms to Epping Green.

It is clear from these facts that the exposure of the Chalk near South Mimms owes much to the uplift of the beds along the anticlinal axis, though the immediate cause of its appearance has been the downcutting of the valley. The valley inliers of Reading Beds farther east are similarly caused. It is necessary clearly to bear in mind that there is, today, no *direct* expression of this folding in the landscape. These minor ripples were incidental to the major folding by which the London Basin was formed; any original landforms due to the folding were obliterated during the long ensuing erosion of later Tertiary times. It is only as a result of the detail of later dissection that such minor folds affect the present outcrops, but the results are notably important in the geography of the district. The Chalk is similarly exposed in anticlinal inliers elsewhere in the London Basin; it forms the hill on which Windsor stands and rises similarly at Purfleet and Cliffe in the lower Thames valley and farther east in the Isle of Thanet. In all these cases the Chalk core of the anticlines stands up as high ground, having been stripped of its Tertiary overburden. Near South Mimms the stripping has not proceeded so far; the anticlinal crest still retains its Tertiary capping, the Chalk being exposed on the southern flanks of the fold. Farther east the anticlinal axis crosses the Mimms valley (*c.* 233026) where the floor is at a level of about 260 feet O.D. In this neighbourhood the base of the Reading Beds is at about 280 feet and the London Clay, if present, would come on at 320–330 feet. It is clear, therefore, that if the beds lay only some 60 feet lower in elevation the valley would here have been excavated wholly in London Clay; the effect of the anticlinal upheaval in extending the outcrop of the Chalk up the valley is thus clearly demonstrated.

DRIFT DEPOSITS

Much of the area is covered by drift deposits, of which the highest and oldest element is the Pebble Gravel. This everywhere caps the high ground (the 400-foot plateau), but in the east of our area it descends below this level, as in Hatfield Park, and around Essendon and Little Berkhamstead. There is no reason to doubt that the deposit was spread uniformly at what is now the 400-foot level, but has been locally reconstructed by downwash and slumping at lower elevations, notably during the glacial period.

The glacial deposits (gravel and boulder clay) occupy the north-west corner and the northern edge of the ground shown on the sheet, here forming part of the great tongue of drift which occupies the Vale of St Albans. It is important to notice, however, that boulder clay outliers, proving the presence of ice, occur on the high ridge between Potters Bar and Epping Green, giving an indication of the conditions under which the Pebble Gravel was disturbed and reconstructed in places.

Of special significance in our present study is the tongue of boulder clay and associated gravels which projects southward from Hatfield to Welham Green. At the latter place the base of the drift climbs as high as 270 feet, but for the greater part its outcrop is marked by a shallow valley extending from Marshmoor to Hatfield and followed by the main road and the railway. At Warren Far End (225077) a well penetrates 58 feet of drift resting on Chalk at about 240 feet O.D. It is clear, therefore, that the drift marks a considerable pre-glacial valley, which must have been occupied by the ancestor to the present Mimmshall Brook before the advance of the ice.

Valley drifts (gravel and alluvium) are well developed only on the floor of the Mimms valley. Near Water End they attain a thickness of 20–30 feet.

DRAINAGE PHENOMENA—SWALLOW HOLES

We may now give attention to the famous swallow holes at North Mimms which are in some respects unique in southern England and owe their origin to the combination of the local features of 'solid' and 'drift' geology which we have briefly reviewed.

Over the central parts of the London Basin the permanent underground water-table, where it has not been lowered by the pumping of wells, lies at the top of the Chalk or in the over-lying Tertiary sands. This means that all open passages in the Chalk are water filled and wells penetrating the water-table are filled by flow along joints and fissures. On the higher margins of the Basin the upper part of the Chalk is dry, the water-table emerging at the surface only in those valleys occupied by permanently flowing streams. This is the condition we have met with in the North Downs and it recurs throughout the Chiltern Hills. At the margin of the Tertiary outcrop either of two conditions may prevail. If the Chalk water-table is here at the surface, the water space beneath the Tertiary cover is full and underground flow from the higher Chalk country must break out in springs, as, for example, near Ewell and Clandon in Surrey (p. 117). If it is below the surface, water draining from the Tertiary tract immediately disappears down fissures on reaching the Chalk,* and these may be widened by solution into swallow holes, which appear at the surface as more or less vertical conical or cylindrical passages. This is the condition met with everywhere along the margin of the Tertiary outcrop between Watford and Hertford. Beneath the high summits of the Chiltern Hills the water-table stands at about 400 feet above sea-level. It descends south-eastward towards the great trough of the Vale of St Albans, drained by the Lea and the Colne. These are fed by surface springs, as at Woolmer Park, just north of our present area. From evidence thus given, combined with that of numerous wells, it is clear that the general level of the Chalk water-table along the Tertiary margin in our area is between 150 and 200 feet O.D. We have seen that the Chalk has been lifted exceptionally high by local folding in this area and, as a result, the Tertiary edge lies in places as much as 100 feet above the water-table. All water draining from the Tertiary outcrop is thus subject to leakage into the Chalk and many swallow holes are found on or near the Tertiary edge. In many cases the downward

* It is important to notice that the effects we are describing are not due to the *porosity* of the chalk; the pore spaces are indeed generally filled with water, but this is firmly held and does not flow freely, if at all. The *permeability* of the chalk resides in its fissured condition, a characteristic it has in common with the harder and older limestones which give rise to 'Karst' country.

movement of water begins as soon as surface drainage passes from the London Clay on to the sandy Reading Beds; the true swallow holes then form beneath the thin sandy covering and, as it is enlarged by solution, the overlying sands collapse into the hollow formed, causing a characteristic dimple at the surface. Such swallow holes marked by 'solution subsidence' at the surface are not necessarily continuously active; they may function only at times of exceptionally heavy surface run-off, or may be completely abandoned. But along the floor of the main Mimms valley the Chalk has been attacked by the considerable and continued flow of surface drainage from the London Clay country to the south since it was first exposed by erosion. There is thus steady leakage along the course of the stream from a point near South Mimms where it first strikes the Chalk. From near Mimms Hall downstream swallow holes are numerous in or near the course of the stream and at Water End the great terminal swallow hole will be found. The whole of the surrounding area here is honeycombed with dimples due to solution subsidence. Close by, the tributary stream following the northern edge of Poterells Park also disappears in a terminal swallow hole.

A visit to Water End will exhibit the drainage in one of three conditions. After a long rainless period the channel may be dry here, with no water entering the terminal hole. If we follow the course upstream we shall find one or another of the neighbouring holes receiving the surviving remnant of the surface flow. Under extreme conditions such flow may terminate as much as a mile to the south, east of the Castle Mound, where the channel has cut an easily identified little river cliff into its eastern bank. Generally, however, flow is maintained farther north than this and the condition at once most typical and most impressive is where the large hole at Water End takes the whole of the surface drainage. After sudden heavy rain, the descending flood is more than can be accommodated by the terminal hole and its neighbours. The area then becomes, temporarily, an extensive lake, and the overflow is carried by the normally dry channel to the Colne at Colney Heath. These conditions were well seen following a thunderstorm in June 1936 which caused a local rainfall of about 4 inches. The resulting mass of water filled the depression at Water End, and flooded the main road, holding up all traffic. Twenty-four hours later the water level had fallen appreciably and after a further two days the depression was dry, with the terminal hole again functioning normally. No such flood had occurred for fifty years, but similar less extensive filling of the 'lake' is of fairly frequent occurrence.

It has been demonstrated that the underground flow of water entering the swallow holes is contributed, in part at least, and probably wholly, to the Lea drainage; dyes put in the stream at Water End have been detected at springs in the Lea valley between Woolmer Park and Broxbourne. We have seen that the original flow of the Mimms stream was to the Lea at Hatfield. The drift filling of the Marshmoor valley temporarily diverted the drainage to the Colne but as the valley was later deepened and the Chalk completely laid bare, the water came again to pass underground to the Lea system, except under conditions of exceptional flooding when part of the water reaches the Colne by surface overflow.

The continual discharge through swallow holes of a large volume of water into the Chalk causes, as might be expected, a local raising of the water-table. Along the margins of the Tertiary outcrop east of Hatfield and west of Radlett the water-table in the Chalk is below 200 feet O.D.; in the intervening area it lies above this level. The Radlett valley also exposes Chalk within the main Tertiary outcrop and here too there were formerly swallow holes in the stream bed, but they have been artificially plugged to maintain the surface flow. Small groups of swallow holes may be found along the courses of the tributaries of Mimmshall Brook. Catherine Bourne, which crosses the St Albans road north of South Mimms, shows a large terminal swallow hole at 219015, though a small surface flow is often maintained beyond it draining to the main stream. Other swallow holes, developed below Reading Sands, occur in Deep Bottom (c. 250035) and also in the valleys north of Northaw.

It will be clear from this brief account that the district offers much of interest and well repays detailed exploration. A walking route which introduces us to the main features may conveniently start at South Mimms, finishing either at Brookman's Park station or returning to South Mimms.

SOUTH MIMMS CHURCH TO RIDGE CHURCH

From South Mimms Church walk southward through the southern part of the village, noting that it lies wholly on the drier and more readily cultivated Reading Beds, here comprising chiefly sand. Go right at the fork, where we cross the junction with the London Clay, either by a rather faintly marked footpath from the road angle beyond the school or by road *via* the turning north of Clare Hall. The site of Ridge is typical of those of the many plateau villages of south Hertfordshire and the neighbouring parts of Middlesex. Though it appears little more than a hamlet today, it is, as we have seen, the 'head' of a narrow strip-parish extending from the clay country into the Vale of St Albans.

Beyond the 'Old Guinea' inn turn right to the church, and locate carefully the beginning of the footpath which runs *north-westward* from a stile at the north-western corner of the church-yard. We are here on the 400-foot plateau but just below the mapped edge of the Pebble Gravel capping, though signs of gravel downwash may be seen in the churchyard and around the village. It is worth while first to follow for a short distance the footpath which runs *westward* from the stile, for this leads us on to the gravel cap and demonstrates the resulting change in soil conditions.

RIDGE CHURCH TO RIDGEHILL

From the westward diversion return to the stile at Ridge churchyard and take the north-westerly path. This path crosses the first long narrow field diagonally, enters the next beyond the first hedge boundary on the left and, crossing the corner of the next field, descends into the shallow valley south of Ravenscroft Farm.

We are here in typical London Clay country and the thick oak-studded hedgerows survive as a reminder of its former forested condition. It is pasture country, with small fields and deep ditches, and its land-use pattern has been subject to little change for a century or more. The Tithe Survey of 1840 shows the southern part of the parish and its neighbour Shenley, then as now, domin-antly in grassland and in notable contrast to the northern part of the two parishes which, lying on the glacial drifts of the Vale of St Albans, were, and have remained, largely in arable cultivation. It was largely the proximity of London and other local urban markets which put the early premium on grassland husbandry. The earlier staples were the hay crop and the pasturing of bullocks, but during the present century the emphasis has been on milk-production. During and since the second World War a larger proportion has been ploughed for wheat; during the last ten years, indeed, good pedigree wheats have been grown in the area, notably on southward facing slopes. This recent 'plough-up policy', here and elsewhere, has been assisted by the possibility of rapid mechanical ploughing for this permits opportunity to be taken of short dry spells. Of these recent changes little will be seen on our present route; the country retains its long-established grassland aspect.

The footpath descends on to the Reading Beds before we reach the road east of Ravenscroft Farm but of these little sign will be seen unless a soil auger is used. On reaching the road cross it and continue northward by Packhorse Lane. After passing Rabley Farm an old chalk pit west of the road shows chalk beneath a thin cover of Reading Beds, and chalk will be seen thrown up by the plough in the fields to the east of the road. As the lane climbs towards Ridgehill we cross the Chalk for a distance of about 600 yards exposed on the southern flank of the anticline whose course we have traced (p. 180). Before reaching the road junction near the point 206022 we have passed back on to the Reading Beds, and beyond the road junction the London Clay forms the hill-top. Turn left here on the old coaching road (p. 191), which runs parallel with the later main road, turning right on to the latter at the Coach and Horses Inn on the summit of Ridgehill.

THE VIEW FROM RIDGEHILL

Take the narrow lane (right) beyond the inn signposted to Redwell Farm (Ridgehill Farm on the map). From the ridge-top here or beyond the farm fine views open up southward over the clay country towards Barnet and northward across the Vale of St Albans to the Chiltern dip-slope. The northward view is best obtained from the first field on the left after leaving the inn; if no crop is standing, permission should be sought at the farm to enter this field. Alternatively, after passing the farm buildings follow the left-hand field boundary northward, west of the pond—the line of the footpath shown towards Coursers Farm; just beyond the first gate a suitable view-point will be found. From either point the view is impressive chiefly because of the sudden change in land use with the oncoming of the glacial drift cover of the Vale. The slope in front exposes Chalk below the Reading Beds, but the floor of the Vale is largely formed of glacial gravel, capped with boulder clay beyond the line of the Colne. Here are large fields, often hedgeless, and the broad sweep of ploughland is almost unbroken by pasture except near the river. Beyond the Vale lies St Albans, situated on a drift-capped outlier of Reading Beds, with the wooded Chiltern plateau in the background; in clear weather the summit of the Dunstable Downs 15 miles distant may be seen. The physiographic interest of the view lies in the fact that the Vale is, as it were, the successor to the earliest Thames valley of which our area bears witness, though as we have seen (p. 42) the history of its later shaping is a long and complex one. When the Thames followed this route north-eastward into Essex it must have been flowing at a level not far below the brink of the plateau on which we are standing. It was diverted from this route during the first glaciation of the area, but the old valley was then further deepened by a stream which must have been tributary to the diverted Thames. Only with the return of the ice of a later and more extensive glaciation were the drifts which cover the present floor of the Vale deposited and thereafter the drainage of the drift-filled trough became shared between the Colne and the Lea.

RIDGEHILL TO WATER END

The continuation of our route follows the ridge-top eastward by the track which passes south of the pond (an old pit in the thin capping of Pebble Gravel, here clearly in evidence). After skirting a wood the path enters the grounds of North Mimms Park where from a point just above the 400-foot contour the view extends across the Mimms valley to the level skyline of the 400-foot plateau marking the course of the Great North Road, beside which stand the B.B.C. aerials at Bell Bar. The path ahead is generally ploughed up, but follow the field boundary to the left until it reaches the main drive through the park south of Cangsley Grove. Follow the southern side of the wood and join the metalled track which runs north-eastward to Water End. It will be noted that the lower part of the minor valley we are following contains no surface stream. The drainage of the upper slopes disappears in swallow holes marked by surface dimples below a group of bushes (c. 219032). These are within the outcrop of the Reading Beds, the

London Clay forming the upper part of the slopes around the head of the valley; Chalk emerges in the valley floor a short distance to the east.

WATER END TO CASTLE LIME WORKS (Alternatively to Brookman's Park)

The main swallow holes at Water End may best be reached by the more southerly of the two footpaths shown on the map which leaves the road near the Woodman Inn. The footpath may afterwards be followed eastward, if desired, to the road westward of Brookman's Park station, distant about a mile. It is better if possible to return to South Mimms by a pleasant and interesting route of about 2½ miles. For this take the old road southward from Water End beside the stream, past Abdale House. This rejoins the main road at the county boundary. About a third of a mile south of this point the old Castle Mound and Bailey will be seen on the western slope of the valley. Adjoining it is the large pit of the Castle Lime Works which expose some 50 feet of Chalk with a thin capping of the overlying Reading Sands. These have been let down by solution into the Chalk in wide cylindrical pipes, but the sand also fills innumerable fissures or 'sheet pipes' and Dr J. F. Kirkaldy has suggested that the section may be regarded as exposing a group of 'fossil' swallow holes comparable with those of Water End but formed in an earlier stage of the excavation of the valley and subsequently abandoned. Permission must be sought to visit this quarry. Close by on the other side of the main road are the swallow holes noted on p. 185 as taking much of the stream water in dry seasons. It may also be noted that we are here close to the axis of the anticline (Fig. 34).

CASTLE LIME WORKS TO SOUTH MIMMS

Return northward along the road and take the bridle track following the county boundary which climbs the west slope of the valley. This rises over the Reading Beds on to the London Clay; the oncoming of the latter is clearly indicated in the path and by a sharp rise of the ground. Beyond the 400-foot contour the Pebble Gravel comes on in force and is well seen along the path and in old pits nearby. It will be agreed that it closely resembles a marine shingle, consisting almost entirely of rounded stones, chiefly flints, but with white quartz prominent amongst the smaller stones; Lower Greensand Chert is not found here. Some of the ground north of this path has recently been cleared and re-planted with conifers. Until the growth of these obscures it, an instructive northward view will be obtained here, of the northward opening of the Minns valley into the Vale and of its now drift-plugged entry into the Marshmoor depression (p. 182). Beyond the planted ground the path enters a stretch of typical oakwood, which serves at least as a modified sample of the former widespread forest cover. The path finally descends and joins the road at the south lodge of North Mimms Park. Here turn left along the road to South Mimms; it first runs below high banks affording poor exposures of the Reading Beds, but traverses the Chalk floor of the Catherine Bourne valley, partly covered with river-gravel, before reaching the main road north of the church.

SOUTH MIMMS AND ITS ROADS

Before leaving the village note may be taken of its general form. There is little sign of clustering or 'nucleation' for it extends in straggling fashion, along what was evidently the original road, for over half a mile. The road is a section of the old coaching road from London to Holyhead which may be traced northward from Barnet via Dancers Hill and Mimms Wash. It passes thence through the village to and beyond the summit of Ridgehill, cross-ing and re-crossing the later main road. This was constructed by Telford in 1826. A century later, in 1927, the Barnet by-pass road was constructed; it crosses its two predecessors at Bignells Corner (227006), offering us, if we wish, a 'text' for the study of the development of the road net and the changing 'geographical values' which it reflects. We may note without further comment that ten years after the opening of Telford's road coaches from the City of London reached South Mimms in 1 hour 40 minutes; the Green Line Coaches now reach the village from King's Cross in less than half the time. It lies, indeed, within effective suburban range of London, as is apparent from the recent growth of its formerly insignificant neighbour, Potters Bar. Had it not been spared in the earlier phase of railway development and survived until an age which had at least contemplated the deliberate limita-tion of the growth of Greater London its characteristics must have long since disappeared. The history of the village, which abounds in material significant for the geographer, has been well recounted by F. Brittain in a work noted below.

References

R. L. SHERLOCK and R. W. POCOCK: 'The Geology of the Country around Hertford' (*Mem. Geol. Surv.*, 1924).

S. W. WOOLDRIDGE and J. F. KIRKALDY: 'The Geology of the Mimms Valley.' *Proc. Geol. Assoc.* 48 (1937), pp. 307–15.

J. F. KIRKALDY: 'Solution in the Chalk of the Mimms Valley, Herts.' *Proc. Geol. Assoc.* 61 (1950), pp. 219–24.

E. C. WILLATTS: 'Middlesex and the London Region' (Report of the Land Utilization Survey No. 79). This includes a special study of present and former land use in the parishes of Ridge and Shenley, with a full description of the agriculture of the region as a whole.

F. BRITTAIN: *South Mymms. The Story of a Parish*. Cambridge, 1931.

11. Highgate and Hampstead

MAPS: One-inch Ordnance Survey, Sheet 160 (London NW)
One-inch Geological Map, Sheet 256 (North London)
It is possible to follow the route on the 1 : 25,000 sheet TQ28 (51/28), but such maps are less satisfactory in urban and suburban areas and it is preferable in this case to use the 6-inch quarter sheets, Middlesex XII SW and XI SE; these are also available as colour-printed geological maps

WALKING DISTANCE (starting at Highgate and ending at Golders Green): 5 miles

ACCESS: The starting point is the Underground station at Highgate on the Northern Line; return from Hampstead or Golders Green

LONDON AND THE NORTHERN HEIGHTS

The summits of Hampstead Heath, and its neighbour Highgate Hill, are the culminating points of the 'Northern Heights' of London. Rising sharply above the northern slope of the Thames valley they give views of the valley itself, and of London and its site. Standing as they do between the present Thames valley and the line of its old course across central Middlesex (p. 39) their vantage points offer an introduction to the general physiography of the North London area and afford also good elementary examples of valley sculpture, spring action, etc. Further, the heights and the streams they nourish have been important elements in the topography of London and their influence can be traced in all stages of its history. For these reasons the route here described well repays study, though it cannot be treated in quite the same fashion as routes in open country.

We may first look rather more closely at the features of the area as shown on relief and geological maps. The former shows our twin summits near the eastern end of a ridge which, beginning at Ealing, east of the lower Brent, terminates in a long spur which descends from Highgate towards the Lea valley. The form of the ridge of course reflects river sculpture by the Thames, Lea, Brent and their tributaries, but structurally it coincides roughly in position with a gentle syncline of which the axis runs from Hornsey to Acton. This has assisted the preservation of the outliers of Claygate Beds and Bagshot Sands which locally cap the ridge. The former survive as small hill-top caps at Hanger Hill, Ealing and south of Willesden Green. Hampstead and Highgate hills rise as independent outliers of Bagshot Sands above a much more extensive mass of Claygate Beds which is continuous from the highest point on the Finchley Road, above Fortune Green, to Mount View Road, Stroud Green.

The surface drainage of the southern slopes of the vale, augmented by springs from the permeable cap rocks, nourishes a number of minor tributaries of the Thames which, though now for the greater part enclosed below ground, were formerly notable features in the topography of London and have left their marks in its place-names. On the southern slopes of Hampstead rise the West Bourne or Bayswater Brook and its neighbour the Ty Bourne (Tyburn Brook). The former flowed to the Thames near Chelsea Bridge; part of its lower course was dammed to form the Serpentine in 1830. The latter flowed past Marylebone (St Mary-by-the-Burn) and entered the Thames by a number of separate distributaries, two of which enclosed the low gravel island of

Thorney in the river-side marshes—the site of Westminster. The valleys of the headstreams of the Fleet River or Holebourne are conspicuous features on the open ground of Hampstead Heath, marked respectively by the Hampstead and Highgate ponds. The two streams united near Camden Town and flowed past King's Cross to a navigable mouth—the Fleet—at the northern end of the present Blackfriars Bridge. The lower course of the Holebourne valley can still be traced along the line of the Farringdon Road and is crossed by Holborn Viaduct. These small streams were important adjuncts to the water supply of an earlier London and before their lower courses were buried they were subject to occasional major floods. The Holebourne was wont to flood at Battlesbridge, the present site of King's Cross, and in 1809 the floods of the West Bourne below Knightsbridge stopped all road traffic between Westminster and Chelsea. In its lower course the Holebourne had sufficient volume and fall to provide power for a number of watermills and justified its alternative name of the Turnmill Brook.

Hampstead, though mentioned in Domesday, remained a small and isolated hill-village for many centuries; it did not attain separate parish status until after the Reformation. The original village lay on the southern slope of the hill near its manor house, at the present junction of Frognall and Frognall Lane. This is just below the base of the Bagshot Sands which provided spring waters to the early settlement. Its later rise, as a spa and fashionable resort, followed the discovery and use of the medicinal (chalybeate) spring below Well Walk on the other side of the hill. Highgate was originally no more than a small tributary hamlet within the manor of Hornsey. Both settlements have later been drawn into the wider net of Greater London and yet retain a measure of isolation and a mellow and even distinguished architecture redolent of their fashionable eighteenth-century past.

In the later pattern of the urban growth the old road routes from London, which controlled the first stages of its tentacle-like expansion, have remained clearly marked features. The Edgware Road, successor to Roman Watling Street, passes below the western end of the Highgate–Hampstead uplands, nowhere rising higher than 150 feet. The road via Hampstead summit to Hendon and Edgware—a subsidiary parallel route—is recorded by Norden in his *Speculum Britanniae* (1593), but of its antecedents we have little evidence. The main road north from London, ancestor of the present Great North Road, climbed to reach the easy-graded water-parting between the Brent and the Colne on the west and the Lea on the east. The original route was via Crouch End and the steep southern face of Muswell Hill, joining the present road at Whetstone. But as early as Norden's time this was falling into disuse; it was superseded by the coach road over Highgate Hill which traversed the Bishop of London's estate on its northern slopes past a tollgate on the site of the present Gate House Tavern at Highgate. It is thus clear that the earlier road traffic was not deterred by the steep climb over the ridge, but in the early nineteenth century (1809-13) Highgate was by-passed by the easier graded Archway Road which traverses an eastern spur of the ridge in a deep cutting, originally projected as a tunnel.

On railway development the high ground and steep slopes of the Northern Heights have exercised a more evident effect. Of the northern trunk lines from London the old 'Great Northern' avoids the end of the most easterly spur of the ridge at Harringay. The old Midland, and London and North Western, lines had their approach to London controlled by the Hampstead heights; they pass respectively to St Pancras and Euston via the narrow bottle-neck between Hampstead and Primrose Hill, both tunnelling *en route*. They are accompanied here by the North London line which, with its continuation, originally the Hampstead and Tottenham Joint Railway, follows the southern foot of the high ground from Brondesbury to Crouch Hill, tunnelling between Finchley Road and Hampstead Heath stations. Not until the Hampstead tube was continued beneath the hill summit to Golders Green in 1907 did the high ground cease to limit the suburban growth of London. Hampstead Heath, originally acquired as a public open space by the Metropolitan Board of Works in 1871, has grown by the addition of Parliament Hill (1889), Golders Hill Park (1898), the northern Heath Extension towards the Garden Suburb (1905) and Caen Wood (1925).

HIGHGATE AND HIGHGATE PONDS

Leave Highgate station by the stairway leading to Shepherd's Hill and beyond the station approach turn right uphill in the main road. We stand here on the Claygate Beds at an elevation of about

14

300 feet, but the ground falls sharply eastward into the coombe-like head of a minor Lea tributary which gives us a view across the Lea valley with Hornsey Church crowning a low mound of London Clay in the foreground. Note the position of the older Highgate station on the surface line from Finsbury Park; it lies in a cutting at the head of this minor valley between two tunnels which carry the line through steep-sided spurs of the main hill mass to the west.

At the cross-roads at the top of the hill turn left up Southwood Lane. In a few yards the steep feature on the right of the road, below a block of modern flats, marks the oncoming of the Bagshot Sands which are exposed in the bank. The road quickly climbs to 400 feet at the junction with Jacksons Lane and continues over the hill summit to the High Street at Highgate village. It may be noted that some of the older houses along the road obtained their water until late in the nineteenth century from wells in the Bagshot Sands before the provision of a piped supply. Turn left in the High Street for about 100 yards to a narrow blind turning called 'Townsends Yard' which gives access to a nursery ground; here there is a good view down the eastward slopes of the hill and across the Lea Valley. On returning to the road turn right and then left along 'The Grove', where the pleasant old houses retain the memory of the Highgate of the eighteenth century. Beyond St Michael's Church the road begins to descend, dropping from the Bagshot Sands on to the Claygate Beds. The base of the former is marked here and at Hampstead by a pebble-bed bound into a conglomerate by ferruginous cement; this helps to emphasize the spring line at the base of the sands. A large block of the rock will be seen on the right of the road opposite the building marked by a tablet as the former Fox and Grapes Inn. Beyond this point turn right down Merton Lane which descends over the Claygate Beds, here about 100 feet thick. At the bottom of the hill and just above the junction with the London Clay turn left along Millfield Lane and follow it for quarter of a mile to the lower end of the last but one of the Highgate Ponds. Some of the dams which hold up these ponds, and the Hampstead Ponds in the neighbouring valley, are believed to date back to the sixteenth century when a first effort was made to lay the local springs under contribution for the water-supply of London. The project was later carried further by the

Hampstead Water Company incorporated in 1692. Early in the nineteenth century before the consolidation of water resources under the Metropolitan Water Board, this old company supplemented the surface supply by a series of local wells and pump houses.

THE VIEW FROM PARLIAMENT HILL

Cross the valley floor by the path north of the last of the ponds and climb the slope ahead to the summit of Parliament Hill. This gives beyond question at once the most extensive and instructive available view of London and the central parts of the London Basin. If visibility is good a half-inch map is necessary for the study of the view and the identification of distant features. (Bartholomew's Half-inch Map, Sheet 30, will be found serviceable.) The crest of the North Downs is in sight from west of Dorking eastwards to Knockholt Beeches and beyond; on rare occasions Leith Hill is visible through the Mole gap. Westward the view is obscured by trees, but eastward it ranges far down the Thames valley in southern Essex, with the high ground of Brentwood forming the limit. On many occasions these more distant features are obscured by haze, reinforced by London smoke, but a large part of the foreground remains for study when visibility is no better than moderate. Few of the familiar landmarks of London itself cannot be identified, but the panorama is chiefly valuable for giving some sense of the Lower Thames valley and the London region as a whole. The distinction between the high northern bank (Middle, 50-foot or Taplow Terrace) and the low southern bank (Flood Plain Terrace) of the Thames is clearly seen. The High (100-foot or Boyn Hill) Terrace is not preserved in the immediate foreground, but it caps the low ridge at Copenhagen Fields (under which the main King's Cross line tunnels) and expands beyond, around Barnsbury and Islington. Rising above the valley floor on the Surrey side, the low plateau of Putney Heath and Wimbledon Common, the 'Southern Heights' or Sydenham and Forest Hill, and Shooter's Hill (dominating the plateau of Greenwich Park and Blackheath) can be clearly made out. The summit of Shooter's Hill attains the general 400-foot level, represented also at Hampstead and Highgate, while the summit of the Sydenham ridge only just falls short of it. It is evident that the Thames valley has been excavated below this general plateau level; between Hampstead and the Sydenham ridge it is 10 miles wide and 400 feet deep.

PARLIAMENT HILL TO KEN WOOD AND HAMPSTEAD LANE

On leaving the summit walk northward along the ridge of which Parliament Hill forms the termination, keeping as closely as possible to the crest. It is capped throughout by the Claygate Beds, formerly worked in old brickyards on its western side, and forms the divide between the two main headstreams of the Holebourne. After passing the tumulus (undated) on the eastern slope we reach a cross-track, but continue forward up the slope in a north-westerly direction. In about 100 yards we cross the base of the Bagshot Sands clearly marked here by a feature, and except after long dry weather, by the seepage of water. A short distance beyond we reach the fence bounding the grounds of Ken Wood House; cross this by a swing gate and taking the left fork continue northward by a path over open ground. This runs just above the base of the Bagshot Sands, skirting the head of two shallow valleys draining to the Ken Wood lake and fed by springs at the Bagshot junction. The path leads us to the West Lodge of Ken Wood in Hampstead Lane, but just before entering·the road turn by a narrow track uphill (right) into North Wood. This leads us just above the lip of an old pit in the Bagshot Sands and gives excellent surface exposures in a downwash of the Pebble Gravel which caps the hill to the west. Here, mingled with the flint and small quartz pebbles, small pieces of Lower Greensand Chert may be found. They must have been brought from the Dorking district by an ancestor of the Mole flowing to join a Thames which followed a line far north of its present valley. This evidence, taken with that of the view from Parliament Hill, enforces an elementary if surprising physiographic lesson. The transport of the chert now found on the highest hill-tops of the district evidently took place before the excavation of the present lower Thames valley, at a time when these same hill-tops represented not the highest but the lowest ground of the area.

HAMPSTEAD LANE TO WEST HEATH AND HAMPSTEAD

Return to the road at West Lodge and turn left uphill towards the Spaniards Tavern. At the first turning on the right (Winnington Road), the northward view extends across the lower ground of Finchley (conveniently marked by the red chimney of the Squires Lane Electricity Station) to Mill Hill and Barnet where the summits again reach the 400-foot level. The low Finchley plateau comprises boulder clay resting on glacial gravel deposited in the broad hollow between Hampstead and the northern hills formerly excavated by the Thames (Figs. 15, 16).

Follow the Spaniards Road southward over the heath; near the inn a small patch of Pebble Gravel caps the Bagshot Sands which have been extensively dug in times past on Sandy Heath, west of the road. Here the hummocky ground has since been recolonized by scrub and woodland. At Whitestone Pond turn right across North End Road to the open hill-top west of the pond. This gives a view across the undulating plain of western Middlesex, above which rise Harrow Hill (also capped by Bagshot Sands), Oxhey Hill, and the long ridge followed by the county boundary from Bushey Heath eastward to Brockley Hill. Nearer at hand the broad trough formerly occupied by the Thames is seen. Glacial deposits cap the hill at Hendon, marking the floor of the old valley which, however, has been much dissected by the Brent and its tributaries.

From the other side of the Spaniards Road the view extends south-eastward over London down the Vale of Health, the head of the western branch of the Holebourne. The ground drops steeply into the head of the Vale and the base of the Bagshot Sands occurs at the foot of the slope within a few yards of the road. The north-western and south-eastern prospect from this famous view-point enables us to compare the dimensions of the Thames valley (p. 198) with those of its predecessor before the chief glaciation. If we ignore the more recent dissection of the floor of the latter, both its depth and its width are about half those of the present Thames valley through London.

WEST HEATH TO GOLDERS GREEN—HEATH VEGETATION

From here the return can be made, if desired, from Hampstead Tube station, distant about half a mile at the southern end of Heath Street. If time permits, however, it is worth while to continue the route to Golders Green across West Heath. Descend north-westward from the view-point west of Whitestone Pond, following the line of the little valley which drains to the Leg of Mutton Pond below the Bagshot junction. The upper slopes of the Bagshot Sand here display the Grass-Heath Association, the most frequently occurring grass species being Common Bent (*Agrostis tenuis*), the Creeping Soft-Grass (*Holcus mollis*), the Wavy Hair Grass (*Deschampsia flexuosa*) and the Purple Moor Grass (*Molinia caerulea*). Together with these are species like Sheep's Sorrel (*Rumex acetosella*) and the Narrow-leaved Plaintain (*Plantago lanceolata*). The sward is varied with abundant Gorse and Bracken, the whole forming a highly characteristic plant community. Older records show the presence of the several species of heather and its common associate on sandy soils, the Bilberry. These are now very rare and no areas of the true Heath Association survive. The valley floor on West Heath was formerly occupied by a natural bog characterized by plants of the 'Wet Heath Association', locally dominated by the Bog Moss (*Sphagnum*), responsible for peat formation. The bog has been drained, but near the stream damp-loving species common in the Wet Heath Association are still conspicuous, e.g. the Creeping Willow (*Salix repens*), the Mat Grass (*Nardus stricta*), the Purple Moor Grass (*Molinia caerulea*), together with Yorkshire Fog (*Holcus lanatus*) which grows in rank patches in wet hollows.

The lower slopes of West Heath carry Hawthorn and Birch scrub, a stage in succession to 'Dry Oakwood'. The lower slopes of the Hampstead upland still carry ample relics of the former cover of oakwood which probably extended over at least the lower part of the heath. In these woods the dominant tree is the Dry Oak (*Quercus petraea*) with an undergrowth of Hazel or Hornbeam. Where such woodlands are cleared but naturally re-colonized, the Birch (*Betula pendula* and *B. pubescens*), free of the competition of the oak and of its shade, spreads rapidly. This is the probable history of the lower wooded part of West Heath, where the oak is sparingly present, but the dominant tree is the Birch, together with Hawthorn and Blackthorn. Above the Leg of Mutton Pond the valley floor descends on to the London Clay and here marsh species increase, while the head and margins of the pond provide a good example of the Reed Swamp Association dominated by species like the Common Reed (*Phragmites communis*) and the Great Reedmace (*Typha latifolia*).

Turn right on the broad track beyond the pond and follow it back to North End Road over the lower part of the Bagshot Sands. On reaching the road turn right uphill to examine the roadside cutting in the Bagshot Beds capped locally by gravel downwash. On returning follow the road down to Golders Green station—rather more than half a mile.

12. The Lea Valley and Epping Forest

MAPS: One-inch Ordance Survey, Sheet 161
1 : 25,000 Ordnance Survey, Sheets 51/39 and 51/49
One-inch Geological Survey, Sheets 256 (North London) and 257 (Romford)
Most of the relevant geological information is shown on the route map (Fig. 35)

WALKING DISTANCE: about 7 miles

ACCESS: by train (frequent service) from Liverpool Street or intermediately to Chingford station, or by one of the following bus routes to the same place
102 from Golders Green via Palmers Green and Edmonton
145 from Dagenham
38 from Victoria

Defoe in his *Tour through England and Wales* (early eighteenth century) wrote 'probably this forest of Epping has been a wild or forest ever since this island was first inhabited and may show us what the general face of the island was before the Romans landed in Britain'.

This statement may be accepted as essentially accurate. There are indeed other heavily wooded tracts both in the Weald and the London Basin but in none perhaps is the probable character of the original widespread forest cover of our region more clearly and strongly recalled. The following excursion can thus make a contribution to our understanding of the historical geography of the area, the more so since it includes a visit to one of the few inhabited sites of the Early Iron Age near London.

The route also affords wide vistas over the lower Lea valley, in all respects the largest and most significant physical feature in the North London area.

Of the 6,000 acres of woodland placed in the charge of the Corporation of London in 1878 as a public open space, the greater part occupies the crest and flanks of the narrow ridge which here separates the Lea and Roding valleys. The ridge trends from NE–SW, and probably marks the continuation of the gentle syncline to be noted at Hampstead (p. 35). Its higher parts are continuously capped by the loamy Claygate Beds (pp. 4, 10, 35), locally

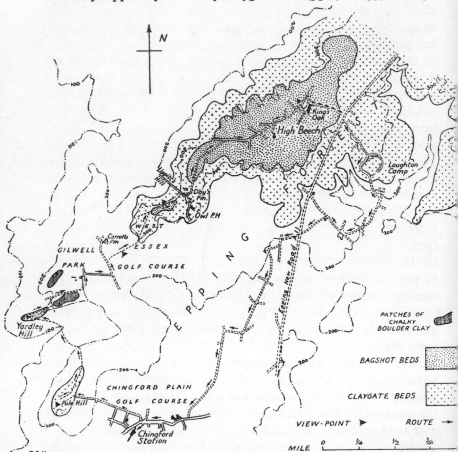

Fig. 35.   Sketch-map of the route between Chingford and High Beech
(Epping Forest)

surmounted by the succeeding Bagshot Sands (Fig. 35). Both formations are locally covered by thin 'drift deposits', gravel and boulder clay, while the adjoining lower ground is everywhere situated upon the London Clay.

The great trough of the Lea valley to the west of the ridge is markedly asymmetrical in its form, with a long gentle western slope preserving a flight of river terraces and a steep eastern slope (Fig. 36). It is clear that the river Lea slipped steadily eastward during the cutting of the valley by reason of the local easterly dip which here affects the rocks which are traversed by a gentle 'monocline' trending from north to south. The valley thus presents a beautiful example of 'uniclinal' (or 'homoclinal') shifting and this has conferred on the western slopes of the Forest ridge something of the aspect of an escarpment (see reference 1 quoted below). There are few steeper London Clay slopes anywhere in the area and their general instability is marked by considerable land-slips.

Leaving Chingford station, cross the station approach and the main road beyond to Connaught Avenue opposite. Turn right along Farnley Road which leads into an unmetalled road, 'Forest View', skirting the southern edge of the golf course on the wide grassy expanse of Chingford Plain. Turn left (westward) along the road or the grass edge beyond it and climb the western slope of Pole Hill, which marks the south-westerly termination of the Forest ridge. On nearing the summit turn left (southward) to the obelisk (partly obscured by trees) which marks the summit. This lies on the Greenwich meridian and was erected by the Astronomer Royal in 1824 to indicate the direction of true north from the transit telescope at Greenwich Observatory.

The hill is capped by the Claygate Beds above London Clay and these are exposed in an old pit east of the obelisk. But the main attractions of this spot are the wide views obtainable westward and southward. The westward view is seen again to great advantage later: the southward view embraces the City of London, with Shooter's Hill, above Woolwich, or the North Downs on the southern sky-line. This view is worth careful study preferably with the aid of field-glasses.

Our further route is northward and it is convenient to return to the eastern side of the ridge following the woodland boundary along the western edge of the golf course. Where the footpath

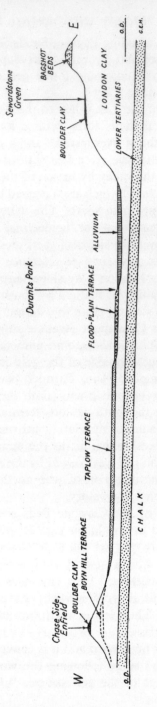

Fig. 36. Section across the Lea valley east of Enfield

forks take the left branch over the crest of the ridge beyond which it descends by an open glade into a steep-sided tributary of the Lea. Cross the stream on the floor of this little valley by a wooden foot bridge and ascend the hill in front in a half-left—i.e. NW— direction to the summit of Yardley Hill (382959). The slope is partly covered by densely grown hawthorn scrub which has colonized old pasture land. Occasional seedlings of oak, ash, willow and blackthorn may be noted. The vegetation here (on London Clay) is comparable with that we have seen on Ashtead and Epsom Commons (pp. 74, 75) and may be regarded as a stage in succession to fully grown oakwood. The hornbeam, a tree very characteristic of Epping Forest, is also abundantly in evidence. An interesting vegetation detail arises from the fact that the hill summit retains an outlier of the Chalky Boulder Clay and although there is no direct evidence of the drift capping, apart from the rather stony soil, the presence of a chalky subsoil is indicated by calcicolous plants such as clematis and salad burnet.

The view of the Lea valley from this point is worth careful study and gives good opportunity for map-reading exercises.

On leaving the view-point follow a narrow track eastward along the crest of the ridge through the scrub. Here the transition from thorn scrub to oakwood may be observed, with hawthorn, blackthorn and bramble persisting as undergrowth beneath the oak canopy.

On reaching a crossing hedge turn left along it down the northern slope of the ridge and right at the foot along a broader track (Gilwell Lane) which threads its way through a narrow coppice. At the top of a rise turn left past the entrance gates of Gilwell Park (the training centre of the Boy Scouts Association) and then right along its entrance road which leads to the public road at 390963. Turn left along this for about 200 yards and take a signposted footpath on the right. This traverses the West Essex golf course and as it rises gives an instructive view back over the ground we have traversed. The most conspicuous foreground feature is the broad flat below us with its surface just above 200 feet O.D. On this surface lies small detached masses of boulder clay, as at Yardley Hill, and the flat evidently marks a stage in the excavation of the Lea valley, the stage indeed at which the ice entered our district. The boulder clay west of the Lea valley, as e.g. at Enfield, is found resting at the same 200-foot level (Fig. 36). This is the same level, we may recall, as the extensive flats in the Mole valley (p. 33) and throughout the northern Weald. Here then is part of the evidence by which we can roughly date the '200-foot platform' in the Wealden area. In the North London area the boulder clay often climbs to higher levels than this (cf. p. 183) but it rarely if ever descends below the 200-foot contour; it is a fair conclusion therefore that the valleys were cut down to about this level when the ice advanced into the district.

At the top of the slope the path turns left and follows the edge of the golf course with a hedge on the right-hand side. Indications of the oncoming of the sandy Bagshot Beds and of a thin cover of high-level gravel are seen in the ditches. The path also affords fine views across the Lea valley, with glimpses of the white tower of Waltham Abbey and of the widespread glass-houses of the famous local market-garden industry.

The path at length reaches a crossing lane, along which turn right for a few yards to find the continuation of our path here a fenced track between a rose-nursery and a group of farm buildings. The path crosses some plough land on the Claygate Beds. As a whole this is a pasture-land area and where arable land occurs as here, it is nearly always located on the lighter soils. The path continues its north-easterly line, becoming again a fenced track, 'Pepper Alley', which leads to a lane west of Wallsgrove House. Here turn right and follow the road to High Beech. This scattered hamlet occupies the summit of a large outlier of Bagshot Sand covered at the surface by a thin sheet of pebbly gravel. This is the same gravel as we have found on the summits of the Hertfordshire Hills.

The westward view from High Beech is restricted by trees, but the level crest of the South Hertfordshire plateau is well seen; landmarks on this skyline are High Barnet Church and the B.B.C. aerials at Brookman's Park, south of Hatfield.

Turn eastward into the woodland from High Beech following the northern boundary fence of the enclosure behind the King's Oak Hotel. Continuing in this direction through beechwood, the main Epping road is reached in less than ¼ mile, at the point 416980. Cross it and turn right at once along the lower of three broad tracks, which runs close to the 250-foot contour line. It soon brings us to the embankment of Loughton Camp on its western side and turns right along the outer side of the bank, following it round to the southern side. We are here in the heart of the forest and several small diversions are worth while, but we may first detail the route returning to Chingford. In following this route the 1 : 25,000 sheet 51/49 will be helpful. Turn right by a track leading downhill from the southern edge of the 'camp'. This leads through oakwood of the wetter type on the London Clay. These contrast with the beech and birch woods on the lighter soils of the plateau above. Cross a foot bridge in the glade in the valley bottom and ascend the other slope of the valley by a broad track trending roughly south-west. This leads to the Loughton–High Beech road near a keeper's cottage and a large pond. Here turn left and watch for another track left, passing another cottage which leads across to the Epping road at the milepost (Epping 4 —London 11). Cross the road here and continue forward to another parallel minor road. This may be followed left, forking right at Palmer Bridge to Connaught Water, beyond which turn right in the nearby road for Chingford. But it is better to turn left for a short way along the minor road and then enter the woodland to the west of it, picking up a broad forest track which leads us southward to a prominent oak tree (Grimstons oak) at the north-east corner of Buttonseed Corner. Here turn right and then left to emerge on Chingford Plain, within sight of Queen Elizabeth's Hunting Lodge close to Chingford station. This part of the walk has led us through a characteristic stretch of the 'lower forest'—wet oakwood with thick undergrowth, in which holly trees are notably prominent. From the rising ground by the Hunting Lodge we may look back over this flat stretch of oakwood to the brink of the Bagshot outlier at High Beech clothed with beech-woods.

References and further Notes

1. A. K. WELLS and S. W. WOOLDRIDGE: 'Notes on the Geology of Epping Forest.' *Proc. Geol. Assoc.* 34 (1923), p. 244.
2. L. S. BAYES: 'A Historical Sketch of Epping Forest.' *The London Naturalist* (1943), pp. 32–43.

3. R. COLES: 'The past history of the Forest of Essex.' *Essex Nat.* 24 (1934), p. 115.

4. W. ADDISON: *Epping Forest: Its Literary and Historical Associations.* J. M. Dent (London), 1945.

5. R. PAULSON: 'The Beechwood: Its Canopy and Carpet.' *South Eastern Naturalist* (1926), p. 24.

6. S. H. WARREN: 'Report on Excavations in Loughton Camp.' *Essex Nat.* 22 (1929), p. 117.

Glossary

This brief glossary is offered in order to explain a few of the technical terms used in the text, but references should of course be made to the fuller treatment of the subject available in the standard works on physiography, plant ecology, soil science, etc.

ALLUVIUM In its widest sense the term covers the whole range of river deposits. In British practice it is usually restricted to the finer-grained deposits of silt or mud which margin a river course and underlie the flood-plain.

CALCICOLOUS (from *Calcicole*) A calcicole is a species of plant confined to soils with a high calcium content.

CLIMAX The culminating stage of a sequence of plant communities on the same site. The climax community is dominated by the largest, and particularly the tallest, plants which can flourish under the prevailing conditions. Usually (though by no means always) the largest plants which can flourish are trees, and when these become dominant the climax community is some form of woodland.

CONSEQUENT A river of which the course was determined by the slope of the original or *initial* land surface.

CUESTA A broad asymmetrical ridge, comprising a scarp-slope and a dip-slope, and formed by the outcrop of a resistant stratum.

DENDRITIC A many-branched drainage system, simulating the normal branching of a tree.

ESCARPMENT The steep slope of the asymmetrical ridge (cuesta, q.v.) produced by the outcrop of a resistant stratum, gently inclined. In this book the words *escarpment* and *scarp* are treated as synonymous.

FLOOD-PLAIN The portion of a valley-floor inundated by normal river floods.

INCISED MEANDER Incised (i.e. 'dug-in') meanders may be either *intrenched* or *ingrown*. The former are essentially symmetrical in cross-section and imply rapid erosion. If incision is slower, giving time for the meanders to continue to develop, the river cutting laterally as well as vertically, the cross-section becomes asymmetrical, a river cliff on one bank facing a 'slip-off slope' on the other. This is the case of the ingrown meander.

INLIER An outcrop of an older, surrounded by that of younger rocks.

INTERFLUVE The ridge between two roughly parallel valleys.

KNICK POINT (German *knickpunkte*, a shoulder-point.) A break in the longitudinal profile of a stream (see figs. 11 and 12).

MESOLITHIC The Middle Stone Age, in Britain dated roughly at about 6000 B.C. The human communities living in southern Britain at that time were without domesticated animals, agriculture or pottery, and lived by 'food-gathering' (hunting and fishing). Most of the known Mesolithic sites in our area are on sandy country, which offered at that time relatively lightly wooded country rich in game. A number of associated flint implement cultures are known.

MONOCLINE A sudden increase in the dip or inclination of strata, followed by a return to the former horizontal or gently inclined posture.

OBSEQUENT A stream having a direction of flow opposite to that of associated consequent streams, i.e. opposite to the direction of slope of the initial land surface. In scarpland country of the type described in this book obsequent streams typically drain the face of escarpments and are tributary to subsequent streams.

OUTLIER The detached outcrop of a younger, surrounded by those of older rocks.

OUTWASH Sand and gravel deposited at the margin of a receding glacier or ice sheet.

PENEPLAIN A lowland of gentle relief—an almost plain surface—often with remnants of higher land standing as hills ('monadnocks') above the general surface.

PODSOL A soil type characterized by pronounced leaching of the surface layers as a result of the downward movement of water, and concentration of the material thus leached—humus and iron compounds—in the layers below. Podsols are typical of land in cold temperate latitudes under coniferous forest cover. They are found in such regions as our own in the areas of sandy or gravelly constitution.

STRIKE A line drawn exactly transverse to the direction of dip in an area of inclined strata. Beds with an east dip will thus have a north–south strike.

SUBSEQUENT Subsequent streams or 'subsequents' are those which have developed along belts of weak structure, commonly in the direction of the strike (q.v.), though sometimes along faults.

SUBSPONTANEOUS Used of a species of plant (e.g. Scots Pine) originally introduced into an area by man, but now regenerating by means of natural seed-dispersal.

SUCCESSION The intrinsic development of vegetation whereby plant communities of increasing bulk and complexity occupy the site in gradual sequence. Succession tends towards the ultimate establishment on the site of a more or less stable community known as the *climax* (q.v.).

SUPERIMPOSED The term applied to a river or drainage system established initially upon a cover of younger rocks which have since been wholly or partly removed from the area by erosion. The courses of such rivers may be quite unrelated to the structure of the older rocks which they now traverse.

TERRACE (RIVER) A portion of a former valley-floor abandoned and left 'high and dry' by the deepening of the valley (see figs. 11, 22, 24, etc.).

TRELLISED DRAINAGE PATTERN Usually with well developed transverse (*consequent*) and longitudinal (*subsequent*) elements, the whole making a fairly regular network.

WIND GAP A dry gap through a ridge, formerly occupied by a stream transverse to the direction of the ridge, the stream having been diverted by river capture.

Index

Lower Tertiaries, 2 (fig. 2), 3 (fig. 3), 9, 12 (fig. 4), 204 (fig. 36). *See also* Eocene, Tertiary
Lullingstone Park, 163
Lullingstone Roman villa, 164
Lynch Hill terrace, 32 (fig. 12)

Maidenhead, 38 (fig. 15)
Maidstone, 2 (fig. 2), 21, 135 (fig. 39), 143, 146, 147
Malden Rushett, 72, 74
Malling Research Station, 136
Marden Park, 150
Margary, I. D., 150, 152, 177
Markbeech, 151
Marlow, 2 (fig. 2), 38 (fig. 15), 41, 83
Marshlands, 50, 144
Mawer, A., 68
Meanders (river), 88, 89, 92, 99. *See also* Glossary: Incised meander
Meates, G. W., 164
Medway, R., 2 (fig. 2), 25, 28 (fig. 10), 31, 33, 34 (fig. 14), 52, 169, 174
Medway basin, mineral resources, 132
Medway gap, 132–47
Medway gravel, 139
Megaliths, 51, 52, 144
Melbourne Rock, 4
Merrow, 59
Merstham, 3 (fig. 3), 59, 60 (fig. 17), 61
Mesolithic, 51 and Glossary
Mesozoic rocks, 5
Mickleham, 28 (fig. 10), 32 (fig. 12), 60 (fig. 17), 70 (fig. 19), 82, 83, 86 (fig. 22), 89–91
Mickleham Downs, 31, 70 (fig. 19), 86 (fig. 22), 91
Microlithic flint implements, 51
Middle Chalk, 4, 15, 16, 121
Mill Hill, 2 (fig. 2), 38 (fig. 15), 41
Milton, 60 (fig. 17)
Milton Brook, 104 (fig. 25), 108, 109
Mimms, 57

Mimms valley, 179–92
Mimmshall Brook, 180
Mimram, 54
Miocene, 7, 26, 168
Mole, R., 2 (fig. 2), 9, 10, 26–34, 34 (fig. 14), 37, 38 (fig. 15), 54, 61, 63, 81, 85–102, 106, 115
Mole gap, 13, 14 (fig. 5), 26–34, 75, 107, 112, 172
Monocline, 35 and Glossary
Moor Park, 36
Muswell Hill, 38 (fig. 15), 39

Nazing, 58
Neolithic, 51, 52, 125
Netley Heath, 4, 15, 75, 129
Netley Heath deposits, 119
New Hythe, 134 (fig. 39)
Newark Priory, 125
Newdigate, 28 (fig. 10)
Newgate Street, 67
Newlands Corner, 15, 117, 119
Norbury Park, 31, 86 (fig. 22), 88–90
Norden, 194
North Downs, 1 (fig. 1), 2 (fig. 2), 4, 6, 8, 11–20, 18 (fig. 7), 58, 69, 94, 96, 101, 133, 172
North Downs trackway, 152
North Mimms, 58, 66, 66 (fig. 18)
Northaw, 66, 66 (fig. 18), 181 (fig. 34)
Norwood Farm (Mole valley), 32 (fig. 12), 100, 101
Nower, the (Dorking), 104 (fig. 25), 106–8
Nower Wood (Headley), 70 (fig. 19), 71 (fig. 20), 78, 83
Nutfield, 61

Oak, 16, 45, 46, 48
Oak-birch-heath (plant community), 177
Oakwood, 73, 83, 96
Obsequent, 22, 23, 114, 151 and Glossary
  gaps, 155
  tributaries of Medway, 148
Orpington, 2 (fig. 2), 9